CAPSULE
STORIES

Masthead

Natasha Lioe, Founder and Publisher
Carolina VonKampen, Publisher and Editor in Chief
April Bayer, Reader
Stephanie Coley, Reader
Rhea Dhanbhoora, Reader
Hannah Fortna, Reader
Kendra Nuttall, Reader
Rachel Skelton, Reader
Deanne Sleet, Reader
Claire Taylor, Reader

Cover art by Darius Serebrova
Book design by Carolina VonKampen

Paperback ISBN: 978-1-953958-06-8
Ebook ISBN: 978-1-953958-07-5

CAPSULE STORIES

STORIES

Second Isolation Edition

Contents

Letter from the Editors

When we published *Capsule Stories Isolation Edition* in mid-April 2020, we thought the coronavirus pandemic would be over within a few months. We wrote in the edition's letter from the editor: "Throughout March 2020, we saw our world rapidly changing. It didn't feel like anything we knew. It was tough to process how quickly things changed—travel restrictions, social distancing, schools closed, stay at home orders, businesses shut down. We didn't have the words we needed to experience this moment in time."

Over a year later, in summer 2021, the pandemic is still ongoing. The virus has claimed more and more lives and left countless people sick, hurt, and broken. Our lives have changed forever. Once again, we are searching for words to describe how we are getting through this and how we are surviving. Our first *Isolation Edition* captured our immediate stories and feelings about the first month of the pandemic. Now, we want to go deeper and explore how our lives have been changed, how we've changed, after living in the pandemic for more than a year.

Second Isolation Edition

You think of how naive you were just a year ago.
How worried you were about things like running out of toilet paper, your career never recovering, your loved ones falling deathly ill. You're still anxious, but it feels different now. It feels longer. Less urgent, less panicked.

Days melt into weeks. You open your laptop one groggy Saturday morning thinking it's Thursday. You place your laptop at the foot of your bed and sleep upside down, just to add some variety to your life. Is it too risky to go get a haircut? When was the last time you saw a stranger smile at you? These are the questions nowadays—forget about the experience you should be capturing. Now, all you know is that awkward silence before the video call ends, as you frantically try to press the button, wearing a fake smile on your face.

But one venture outside will tell you that even though it felt like your life had paused, the rest of the world kept moving. People you know, or don't know, have been lost forever. There's noisy construction on streets you knew intimately, new restaurants replacing your old favorite ones. People are going out as if nothing happened. You feel like the only person who remembers what life was like before, what life is like now. But you'll never forget how the world changed, how you changed. How alone you felt. You will always remember this.

Broken Faucet

Paulette K. Fire

There was a time when we lost track of time. It was a time when it was not safe to be near people. Even people we loved. During that time we had photographs we looked at. Some of the photographs were on a screen. We could talk to the photographs. People said it was almost like the real thing. Sometimes the pictures froze, but that didn't mean we got the time back. The photographs with the babies and their dimpled hands, one-toothed smiles, chubby knees made us sad. We knew we would never hug their baby bodies. They'd be one two three years old before we held them again. The cuter the babies got, the worse it got. The cuteness was unbearable. Our eyes welled up. Tears spilled down our faces. Wet our clothes. Soaked our shoes and socks. When there was talk of a second third fourth wave, we knew we had to shut off the faucets. We tightened and tightened. Our teeth shuffled themselves into new arrangements. Our hearts pounded. Our heads ached. We tightened some more. There was no other choice. When our Nespresso machines broke because some of us were shoving the lever with perhaps too much force to the side, and the machines groaned and screeched and water and coffee grains poured over our kitchen floors, we tried to understand what was happening. People spoke of messages from God and the universe. The poets among us wrote essays about metaphors. The know-it-alls and hysterics said it was a warning. But I had given up on messages and metaphors and warnings. I called the people whose job it was to care for me. I have hope for your machine, the woman at the customer care center said. But when will the machine work the way it's supposed to? I asked this woman with her fine Italian accent. All in good time, she answered. All in good time.

Totally Fine

Paulette K. Fire

Totally fine
is what you are
when you fall down the stairs
hit your head,
only once,
and sprain your knee.
Slightly.

Totally fine
is what you are
when the phone
rings at two thirty
in the morning
and the person on the other end
says, "Sorry, sorry."
And at four forty
in the morning
you're still wondering
did they say,
"Sorry, sorry," or
"Hurry, hurry?"

Totally fine
is what you are
when you take a walk
with your husband and you
trip and grab onto him
and you both wind up
on the ground

---

and a runner stops
to see if you,
the two old people
lying in the grass,
are okay,
and you wave him away
because of course you're
okay.

Totally fine
is what you are
when you're up
in the middle of the night
helping your child
with his chemistry homework
in a class he's about to fail
and the last time you took chemistry
was in 1966.

Totally fine
is what you are
when you find yourself signed up
for a retreat
you don't remember
signing up for
and no one will tell you
when it'll end.
All you know is

here you are.
Standing at the
edge of a cliff

with your toes
hanging over
and a wind gusting
at your back.
Thinking
what the fuck is happening
what the hell now
this is too much.

And you start praying to a god
that you don't even believe in
asking for just one thing
one thing
and you'll never ask
for anything again
because after all
you are totally fine.

The Epley Maneuver

Kelle Schillaci Clarke

By the third day, the dizziness had gotten so bad she was walking at a permanent slant, her left arm hanging lower than her right. She had to use both hands to clutch at walls and doorjambs in order to move safely from her bed to the bathroom.

All we've been through, and this is how I'm going to die, she thought, her eyes squeezed shut as she peed. *Next to the fucking toilet, head bashed in from the fall. Dead on the tile with my pants down. That's how my daughter will find me. She'll be in therapy the rest of her life.*

She was fine if she kept her eyes closed.

"Breathe for me," the doctor said. He moved the stethoscope across her back. She was great at breathing. Years of yoga. *Pranayama.* He had her follow a pen with her eyes, stared into her pupils.

"Okay, let's try something," he said. "Are you able to turn around, so your feet are over here, where your head would normally be?" He patted the raised end of the exam table.

She did what he asked—a good patient—placing her boots on the pillow and sitting at a right angle. *Dandasana.*

"Tilt your head to the left, at a forty-five-degree angle," he said. He was all about angles, she could tell his face was full of sharp ones, beneath his mask. "Now lower yourself back," he said, "slowly."

She engaged her core, lowering one vertebra at a time. She wanted to tell him she'd finished her thirty-day yoga challenge—a "journey" the instructor had called it—missing only one, but doubling up the next day. She didn't mention how her Dry January "journey" had ended by day two.

Besides, he wasn't her regular doctor.

The first time it happened, her daughter had needed help. Her internet connection had been interrupted, or her microphone wasn't working, or maybe she'd retreated to her room, curled into a tiny ball with her thumb in her mouth, regressing. "Mama! I need you!" her daughter had yelled. So she'd stood up quickly, took two steps, and gravity pulled her so hard to the left that she'd fallen, dropping the laptop from one hand, her coffee from the other. Her daughter had screamed, rushed to her side. Her husband, working from the basement, ran up the stairs.

"What's going on up here?" The noise of her fall had interrupted his work call.

She'd sat on the kitchen floor, head tucked between her knees while he cleaned the coffee, plugged in the laptop, and got their daughter back in school. *Everything is fine.* She got up, embarrassed. *Everything is fine,* she kept saying, to herself, to her husband, to herself again.

"Okay," said the doctor, "you're almost there."

When her head reached the table, he told her to let go, release.

"I've got you," he said, his palms handling her skull, fingers down her neck. She let her shoulders sink, felt the slightest pop come from deep within the complicated cords in her neck, which she imagined as a twist of verdant green vines.

"Now, slowly, begin to turn your head to the right," he said. Her head supported safely, made calm by his fingers. A weird sound emerged from her, a whimper she couldn't pretend wasn't her own. The room was so small, the air so tight. He pretended not to hear it, waited a moment, then repeated his request.

His hands guided her head, cradling it like a baby, an object completely separate from the rest of her body, which she could hardly recognize anymore. *Whose body is this?* She could feel every single neck vine shifting, repositioning.

Once she reached forty-five degrees, he held her there, and paused.

"Keeping your neck at this angle, I want you to start sitting up, very slowly."

She couldn't speak, couldn't shake her head no, couldn't open her eyes, for fear the world would spin again. Right now, she was safe. The world was still. His hands were solid.

"Did anything happen this week?" the doctor had asked earlier in the appointment. "Anything out of the ordinary?"

My kid hasn't been in school or indoors with another kid for over a year. I spend hours a day in the freezing cold with other sad moms so our masked children don't forget how to play. My hair has grown so long, so unruly. I've forgotten what it's like to be alone. I'm so lonely I can't fucking breathe.

"Nothing out of the ordinary," she'd said. But maybe she lied. Maybe the world had become such a mess of so many extraordinarily awful events that they'd all blurred into nothing. Maybe she'd missed something. Goddamn. She missed everything.

The doctor loosened his threaded fingers so her head sunk deeper into his warm palms. A tear leaked from her left eye, traveled the crown of her nose, through her right eye, to his hand. This time the sound she made filled the room.

"Shhhh," he said. "Keep your eyes closed."

She did. And the world stopped spinning.

Sand
Stories

Jan Chronister

Charted like virus cases
tides rise, fall, rise,
pull ocean waves.
Full moon reflects
on surface, whitecaps
rustle.

In the morning
I find broken
sunglasses, a spoon,
old buckle,
fishing lines with hooks,
jagged bottles
waiting for naked feet.

Visitors write
messages in wet sand
punctuated with shells,
palm leaves and sticks.
Newlyweds draw
hearts, add the date.

This winter I stay home,
walk beaches in my sleep,
dream of when I can return,
read stories I've missed.

Bookmarks

Jan Chronister

Slick postcards
from the National Trust
for Historic Preservation
come in the mail,
portray places I hope
to visit someday
when this is all over.
Friends send me
handmade page markers,
threads showing in heavy paper.

I read myself to sleep—
detective novels,
British romance.
I can't handle the classics
during house arrest.
I need escape,
guilty pleasure.

I read outside if I can,
acquire knowledge
and tan
simultaneously.
If I learn about
New Jersey geography,
Regency hygiene,
skeletal anatomy,
my time locked up
has been well spent.

Now and Then

Deborah Purdy

Our next-door neighbor talks to herself,
sweeps leaves from one edge
of the sidewalk to the other.

From one window to another
across the street
shadows of cats consider their options.

A day used to mean
something
and most people knew what they were doing.

The flip side isn't an avalanche
but a creeping descent—
a slide into time that isn't itself

but an imposter pretending
to matter, a masquerade of unusual
suspects—hair salons and funeral parlors—

participants among contradictions
and confusion.
In the blur between then and now,

every now and then we think about it—
like the county fair that's folded up
and sailing away.

Quarantine

Deborah Purdy

Tapping her foot's not enough—
she wants to twirl and curve
into rhythm and reel like a flight
of wheels, to swerve out of control,
out of hand, to lightly land in a
measured turn, in tune
with the music and calls.
She wants to stir until dizzy,
to dazzle and dance through wafts
of tobacco and tokens of roses,
to swish and rustle
her skirts into a whir, a flurry of circles
of birds of paradise or prey. She wants to pace
and pivot, swing and spin the hours
into days and roll them into a line
like necessary soldiers. She wants
to change partners like dresses
that waltz by themselves and
she wants to be the belle
of it all.

Happily
Ever After

Linda McMullen

No one ever told me that happily ever after would be so damn *boring*. That it would consist primarily of endlessly scouring pans to liberate them from fish flakes or omelet crusts. And endless games of Where Is the Other Sock? And quilting in the evenings (a traditional, economical, and productive hobby).

Before my marriage, I could make the entire city tilt on its foundations by stepping out of a cab in a minidress and stilettos.

And now—

And now.

I telecommute, I participate in an online Zumba class, I read scandalous novels from bygone ages. I dream of a lover like Lady Chatterley's. I don't wonder why Emma Bovary started having affairs. I envy Moll Flanders for *living*. Don't get me wrong: I still love Steve and I have no intention of breaking my vows. Not to mention that I don't have a man in mind. (Or a woman, come to that.) I just . . . ugh.

Steve remains the mellow center of our home, unfazed by unrelenting domesticity and togetherness. He wears olive-colored fleece jackets and reads the newspaper. My heart withers a little.

"Maybe . . . you're ready to start thinking about a baby?" he offers one evening.

If side-eyes could kill.

"Okay, maybe not," says Steve mildly, and turns the page.

It is a truth universally acknowledged that ennui curdles easily into resentment. This natural flow doubles its velocity when circumstances bar the usual alternatives—volunteer for a cause, go to the gym, join a wine and cheese inflected book club. And there are only so many episodes of *Bridgerton*. (Alas, and bless you, Saint Shonda.)

When Steve sits in the living room, I retreat to the bedroom with my laptop. Words spill from my fingers—on Twitter, then Reddit, then (and I am not ashamed to admit this) Literotica. I compose Regency intrigues, Victorian assignations, midcentury acrobatics in a canoe. Sexual adventure erupts from my fervid imagination into Microsoft Word, and thence to the open-minded expanses of the internet.

I gain a modest following.

I win a contest.

I start sleeping in the spare room.

Steve attempts heartfelt conversations. He asks very reasonably for dialogue. He mostly avoids sniping at me. But he keeps catching me at moments where I'm elsewhere, clawing through my thesaurus for a more elegant synonym for "kaput" (meant to describe an eroding marriage in my new novel in progress). Long after Steve has deposited his house slippers on his side of the bed, I have completed a breathtaking first chapter, and I am soaring.

Euphoric insomnia.

I pad around the house, debating whether to start Chapter 2, when I notice Steve's laptop on the dining room table. He usually remembers to power it down, but now, in the 2 a.m. hour, its still-live, glowing face offers a silent reproach.

I drop my cursor into his address bar to conduct a laughably premature search for erotica publishers when I note that Steve, per his browser history, has Googled:

- virtual counseling
- romance in lockdown
- how do you get your wife to fall in love with you again

I blink at the screen for a few moments; my eyes feel hot. It must be my insomnia. My chin juts out, and I turn the computer off without shutting it down properly.

In the morning I make the coffee and remember to extract the filter and make a respectable breakfast for myself and Steve because it's a civilized thing to do, and possibly because I haven't really done so in a while. Steve sets his jaw and thanks me, then says I'll have plenty of time to write because he has some errands to run. I nod, probably, on my way back to my laptop, residing on my desk in the once-spare room.

He returns with a number of parcels. I hear odd thumps and crinkling plastic and the clink of stemware. At dinnertime I hear the doorbell, and Steve yells, "I'll get it!"

I emerge five minutes later to find the best that our local Uber Eats runners can offer on the good china, a glass of sparkling white at my place at the table, and Steve wearing a fitted dress shirt, open at the collar, and crisp black slacks. He's wearing a cologne I don't recognize, but it smells like a torrid night in a faraway tropical capital.

"Steve . . ."

"Not tonight," he says. "Tonight, I am Stephano, and it is my wish that you will please dress for dinner, and join me."

I had really wanted to get back to Chapter 2 this evening. But . . . he's trying, and if there's anything that romance writing has taught me, it's that rejecting a heartfelt effort really kills the mood.

And there's a spark in his eye I haven't seen in a long time . . .

I don my favorite little black dress and kitten heels, and apply a quick dash of lipstick, mascara, and perfume, in two minutes flat, but I reenter the dining room at a stately pace. Stephano (!) talks to me about the wine—the region, the growers, the family dynasty of growers and tradespeople and connoisseurs. I can almost taste the sunshine on my tongue.

After dinner there are chocolate-dipped strawberries from the boutique downtown.

Then we retreat to the living room, where Stephano wordlessly puts on a salsa album, and we pile the coffee table on top of the couch and dance . . .

And then, hand in hand, we retreat to the bedroom.

there's a spark in his eye
I haven't seen in a long time . . .

Open for Business

Beth Morrow

And after the waitress
Wipes down our menu with bleach
The corners of her soft blue eyes
Return our smiles as she returns
With lemon wedge edged glasses of water

He pushes down his mask,
Takes a sip.
We swivel our stools
Toward each other
Toward the privacy inside
Our wood-framed plexiglass walls.

In the void where no one can see
Between our bodies and the bar ledge
His warm palm
Steadies my knee
As I fold and tuck my mask
Beneath my turned-off cell phone

Whispering a dirty joke,
His lips brush the edge of my ear
And turn on something
I think I felt, once?
(Or maybe just a memory?)
In
Another lifetime,
Another body?

This spark of hope
Competes
In both of us
With the darkness
And sadness
And loss
And grief
And changes
And reality
Of who we were
And where we have been
And who we are
And where we now sit

And everyone can see us
Yet no one is watching
As we laugh like fools

Of who we were
And where we have been
And who we are

Car in
Reverse

D. H. Valdez

During the pandemic, with nothing better to do, my wife and I took up the game of trying to find old places from our past without the use of Google Maps.

Recently, we made it within three blocks of the restaurant we had our prom dinner at before giving in to technology. So close.

Another time, we landed at her great-grandma's house no problem. Impressive, given the fact my wife hadn't seen the house since she was eight. "It used to be brown," she explained as we sipped our coffee and peered at the small blue house. She rolled down her window. The vibe rushed in with the wind.

"How does it feel?" I asked.

"Nice. Kind of like a summer rain."

When she was ready, we kept on driving.

Both of us grew up in Seattle and had played soccer all throughout the city. Locating some of these old soccer fields became our next theme. Some of them were so obscure and fragmented and nearly lost in our minds that even if we used the map, it would have been no use. Kind of like saying, "Okay Google, where's Atlantis?"

We shared our memories, trying to piece together enough details to work on.

"I'm remembering playing somewhere that had a dog park nearby, and there was an urban forest or something on one side. Remember that one?"

"A lot of the fields had that . . . orange jerseys. Did the other team have orange jerseys?"

"Yes!"

"The orange jersey team played at Lower Woodland. Let's go!"

On this day, we cheated and plugged it into our phone. The game changed. It was always about the remembering anyway.

At Lower Woodland, I saw one of my old students riding his bike around the perimeter of the soccer field. Last time I had seen him was when he was with his entire graduating class at their post-graduation all-night celebration. Think pizza, arcade games, and soda. I chaperone every year because it's so fun. But another reason I do it, I think, is to say goodbye one last time. To make and keep one more memory.

Here this student was again. And here I was once more, saying goodbye.

But on to the next one.

"It was on the top of a hill, like in a real neighborhood setting. And it was by an old high school, I think. I remember that you could see the whole city down below."

"I don't remember that at all," my wife said.

I kept repeating the memory aloud, hoping that she would be able to fill in a clue. Each time I said it, the desire to find the field became even stronger. She wasn't remembering. Doubt crept in. Maybe I was wrong. Perhaps the place never existed. I explained this all to her.

"Only one way to find out," she said. "Upward. Let's go up."

We climbed several hills. We found many beautiful views of the city, and we actually ended up finding some old fields that we hadn't even thought to add to our list, but we still hadn't found this particular field, this memory.

We focused on old high schools and googled them, hoping this new tactic would pay off. One former school that we drove to was now an office building, another a hospital. Another still left simply to rot.

No fields nearby.

We decided to try one more spot. Our directions told us that the school was just a half mile away, and as we got closer, the memory deepened.

"I think I remember this street! And going to that Subway for a turkey sandwich after the game," I said, excited.

My wife was happy for me too.

Yet by the school, only a concrete playground remained. "Was this it?"

"I'm not sure," I said. We got out of our car.

"Does it feel right?" my wife asked.

High atop this concrete patch, next to this old school, my wife and I were away from the vibrant city below. We were alone except for the crows, on this gray, nostalgic Seattle fall day.

We stood tight together, remembering.

"I don't know if this is the place," I said. "But it feels good."

Goddess of Knife and Stove

Melissa Sussens

You are in the kitchen,
our favorite refuge

which now, in the pandemic,
is a place of worship at home.

Here, we partake in ritual preparation,
each tender act of creation

a holy service of its own
and you, the goddess of knife and stove.

First, your blade takes the sacrifice of onion;
the pot a sermon of sizzle and sputter,

browning into caramelized embrace.
Next, a dash of rich burgundy

wine, reducing while your fingers
add the sprinkled solace of salt.

Then, flour and water are measured,
you always the alchemist, exact

in your creating. Your hands press,
stretch, coax, mold the bread dough into loaf.

I have never longed to be something else
as much as I long to be that dough pressed

into your palm, right now,
your fingers devout in their knead.

Our home fills with the smell of warmth,
your creation rising into something delicious.

You ladle our bowls full with thick, rich comfort
accompanied by bread and butter dripping

onto our charcoal-gray side plates.
Our red flowered table is all abloom,

an altar of your love for me.
I am home. Through this pandemic

I am safe, sitting across from you;
my taste buds a choir of praise.

Through this pandemic I am safe, sitting across from you

Don't Press Play Without Me

Teya Hollier

He chooses a movie—
usually fast cars,
fists and bullets flying, a deadly
mission to save a loved one.
I choose a movie—
usually a house haunted,
a child possessed, a ghost lingering
in the walls.

The bright flickering screen feeding us
adrenaline of fight and life.

Life lacks adrenaline now.
Life lacks fight.

We plump our tush
on a cushion and consume
sugary sweets salty treats
and an attractive protagonist
with a magnetic will to live.

Another movie another distraction
from our humdrum life.

I want a ghost to haunt the walls.
To scratch and howl, to knock
on doors and fling open cupboards.

To pull off the covers and try
to invade my soul. To quicken
my breath and heartbeat so
I can find fight to push away.
To remember what *will* is.

He wants to drive fast
down a dark, lonely, long road
to rescue me from the Big Bad.
To karate chop his way up the stairs,
to toss knives and dodge bullets.
My screams his beacon, his boost
to remember what life is.
A wild roar in the gut that pumps
the spirit inside you.

Life lacks spirit now.
Life lacks roar.

Press play on a comedy starring
Adam Sandler and Jennifer Aniston
in a hate-love cavort.
Or Kevin Hart and The Rock
poking fun of each other's
hyperbolic opposite size.
So we can remember the feeling
of a rumbling giggle tickling
our throats, breaking through our lips:
a cackled cacophony of unhinged cheer.

Press play on a couple
stranded in a dense, thick forest.
Humans fumbling through a maze
of thin, tall trees whose green-winged
branches tip the skies.
So we can remember how
full of soul Mother Nature is:
how shiny the leaves,
how tweet-ful the birds,
how long-blue the sky.
As the couple fights to survive.
Barely, hardly, one always dies.

To remind us how comfortable
we are in the darkness.
In the warmth within our walls,
in the fullness of our bellies,
in the softness of our mattress,
in the closeness of our bodies.
Nothing is better than this.
And then the credits roll.

He finds another movie
as I tiptoe to the washroom.

"Don't press play without me" I call,
so that he will respond, "I won't!"
and I am reminded
that at least I'm not alone.

I Can't Even Find It in Me to Water the Flowers

Teya Hollier

Instead, they sit on the edge
of the window in the bathroom.
Wilting, shrinking, dying.

He came home the morning of my birthday,
a sun-sized grin, holding a pot of
plump-pink flowers cushioned in soil.

"Why didn't you just get me
a bouquet of flowers?" depression questioned.
"Because these will last longer!" His optimism
like raindrops on a humid day. Refreshing.

Plucked bouquets are low maintenance.
Death's already in action, they can't
live long removed.

Floating in glass, staining
the water in their decay, you toss them
when they are no longer living and pretty.

None of this is your doing.
Someone else snipped them from root,
their death, a natural cause and effect.

The potted plants need care.
I watch them, shriveling,
as I stand in front of the mirror.

Twenty-five pounds down since lockdown.
Panic rising, floating eyes against
sullen skin searching for my missing fat.

My missing energy,
my missing smile,
my missing person.

Anxiety cushioned in
my gut, sprouting till
all food causes chaos.
Killing my appetite.

Sun turning against flower,
flower turning against sun.

"Eat" he says,
"Eat" my mother says,
"Eat" my friends say.

I can't even find it in me to feed the flowers.

Sun turning against flower,
flower turning against sun.

Metamorphosis

Ashley Huynh

A. *homeostasis*
In lecture, we learned that there is
equilibrium in the world
and it manifests in the body.

I can tell you:
hormones are our ruler.
Bones build and break,
scars scab and shed,
insulin and glucose recycle.

Did you know?
Our most natural response to
disturbance is
fever.

If I can think about this year,
it's a weight too heavy,
an anchor on an already teetering scale.
It feels like the universe has dialed up
our biological thermostat
and had us reel
in its festering heat.

Sometimes I wonder
if this paralyzing pain I feel
is God's way of letting
the world's flu
take its natural course.

Will things ever be normal?

B. decomposition
In lecture, we learned that our past,
present, and future lives die every day.
Every millisecond around the sun,
our telomeres, the biological fabric
that etch the stories of our lives,
burn like the ends of a matchstick.

When I thought about how I'd spent
my fleeting twenties,
I pictured much more:
the glittering opal of a foreign skyline,
the citrus blurred vision of bottomless mimosa brunch,
the black silk of a gown that signifies a hello to a new beginning.
These days, my life palette resembles more of
Picasso's Blue Period: monochrome cyan-lit frames
of Zoom, indoors, and online.
The thought of more birthday candles
makes me nauseous.

These days, it feels like the seasons have all
bled into each other, like watercolor
accidentally spilled from a glass.
March melts to summer to spring to fall
yet it still feels like an eternal winter.

The clockwork of life has slowed to a
socially distanced halt and I will be
honest: it's easy to feel so alone in a cage.

C. transformation
In lecture, we learned that our bodies
can be molded like clay.
Synapses spout and bloom,
die and decay, depending on
the seeds we supply it.
Perhaps this whole year is us
preparing our roots.

Survival is our greatest virtue,
resilience our greatest talent.
This hardest time is just our
great hibernation, and like
beasts, we rest and lick our scars,
slumber in this arctic time to heal.

Transformation drives the future
of the world and metamorphosis
is the root to all living.
Humans self-destruct to grow
and caterpillars consume poison to change.
Pain is the source of all rebirth.

As we wait in our waxen chrysalis cages,
dust off our molten wings,
contemplate the world we will be,
spring will thaw.

A Year
Unspent

Sukriti Lakhtakia

Wooden doors at home have swollen in the rainy season,
and shrunk back to the usual, it has been so long—
my friends' nails must have grown many times over,
shirts have faded, new plants have graced windowsills.
Have I grown taller?
My body is now the only acceptable calendar of time:
hair on arms for how many weeks it has been,
those on my legs for number of months,
my brows creeping closer to each other
for how many frowns,
my pale skin for the bright sun lost on our faces.
It has been so long—
the rhinoceros family living above my home
has quieted down, cockroaches at our home
have multiplied and now call it their home.
My father has learned how to cut a fruit.
My sister and I are now the same person,
the patters of our feet around the house harmonize,
my mother has trouble distinguishing our voices.
In these trying times in these trying times,
in these trying times,
I have tried, only to fail at small talk or
to bother with plastic politeness.
The weight of a year unspent
has now eased itself,
I am a friend to myself.

I Have Unlearned My Body

Sukriti Lakhtakia

I have unlearned my body
only to know it again.
I have found it to be plain,
unremarkable—
stripped of the burden of the gaze.
Howmanyever months have passed
and I have spent summer and winter
standing before a mirror.
It's spring now, my body is my body.
It is neither a poem nor a song,
definitely not a metaphor,
and no vision of perfection.
My body is my body—
my breasts, hips, and thighs
regard me with innocence.

An Ode to My Long Hair

Bethool Zehra Haider

Originally published in The Patient Project *in March 2021*

I. Death

In the fall everything seemed to be dying. In an unexpected move to the East Coast, I traded the sunny home I grew up in and its pink roses of August for my first Real Autumn, where plants that once were flowers shriveled into brown stubs. Leaves that once had homes on trees plunged to frigid deaths. Wind that unabashedly pushed animals into their winter tunnels, stealing the life force from the sun, from the world, howled around corners and masqueraded as smoke from our mouths.

In the fall I grew my hair out long for the first time. A lifetime of impulsively short cuts ironically cut short by the longest spell of caution I've yet experienced. But in the fall, when the barber shops were closed and I was too timid to take scissors to my own head, I sat back and watched.

In the fall I died endlessly, each day waking up a new person in the same place, the same cavernous aloneness threatening to drown me. Aloneness is not an adjective, like loneliness, but a physical being. My Aloneness. It accompanied me in the solemnity of my bedroom just as it followed me near people, near animals, near crowds of voices, near lights. Aloneness that creeped into my visage in the veins under my eyes, that bloomed a shade of lavender in circles I had never seen before. Aloneness that created deep veins under my skin, like roots of a willow, climbing up my arm. Aloneness that rendered me a tree falling silently in a forest—unheard, unseen, unknown. Am I a person at all, I often thought in the fall. Am I a person at all, when I am alone by myself?

II. Sin

To kill is a sin, so I've heard. To allow the darkness inside of you to spill out onto another being—it's a sin. To steal away the love of God by spoiling his biggest gift. A sin.

But what about the man who snips a daffodil to hand it to the one he loves? What about the gardner, pruning the bark of a tree to replant it and once more allow it to grow? What about the wind, which, in its recklessness, blows out the daintiest candle's flame? Are they, too, sinners?

I don't know the answer. So I hold myself still, in fear. I refuse to hurt a living being. I refuse to cut my hair. I pick up leaves from the ground but can't pluck a single flower. I let my hair grow long. Long, long, long. Unable to snip that which my body produces, I watch as my hair grows. With a tiny pigtail that hardly graces my shoulders, my reflection is familiar. It gets longer and longer, gracing my back, my arms, my waist. My reflection morphs and becomes someone else, someone I do not know. The temptation to return to my old self draws me to scissors.

But I cannot sin. I do not sin. Who am I to call forth such authority, to be the god of hair? Who am I to create such death?

III. Time

My long hair tells me how long it's been. I feel it all so strangely, the weight of many months and people and time. They grow upon me like ivy, their slick tentacles dragging into my skin, staining me. Time exists in a bottle, sealed shut. I swallow it whole and feel it expanding within me.

I busy myself by growing roots. When the doors open again and the sun tells me it's spring, perhaps they will be too deep for me to move.

A body changes so slowly, we hardly notice. My hair grows, and I don't see it until months later. The rain falls drop by drop. It pools in a micrometer. A millimeter. A centimeter. Minute by minute, we fail to notice. But suddenly, a puddle. Suddenly, a pool.

I did not notice, but suddenly I am sprouting leaves.

My skin grows thicker. Underneath, I see layers of myself from past selves. I live inside myself, watching my hair grow. I do not move. I am like the trees that stand outside my window. But where time stole their leaves, time has given me mine.

IV. Growing

Growing your hair requires strength. It requires restraint, like iron on wrists. It requires loss. Loss of control, which I once kept so firmly in the tiny length of my hair, the shortness of my bangs. It requires death, in ways, of the person who I was without it. It requires focus: focus upon the new person I will become. The new person who braids her hair now, every night. Each pleat a promise to keep going. Each pleat a tally on the wall.

Growth requires powerlessness against something else. A force, which refuses to stop, which wishes, at all costs, in all scenarios, to continue blooming. Little blossoms of sunlight inside, pushing us upward. What is this force but God? The little thing that makes a seed grow. That's God too. The push inside of me, which causes my hair to grow. That's God too. I know it is. Because despite this winter, when everything dies, somehow I keep growing.

Everything Holy

Jenne Hsien Patrick

reappears in the tender
green shoot of a squirrel bitten
bulb left on top of the soil
next to a new, frantic hole
exactly where I had planted it deep.
I imagine it was the one I've seen,
the fat squirrel who shares the plum tree
with the robins, who are themselves
just a few weeks away from song.
Last year the trees sung with bloom
a little too early, right before we knew
everything would change. The light
is now the same thin rising, days becoming
longer again. The year now dares
to repeat like the days and I push the bulb
back into the earth, its tiny emerald stalk
poking out, whole. It isn't quite spring
yet, it is too early. Only a couple months
more. The sun still sets near five o'clock.
I can't help but admire whoever gnawed it,
who was so lucky to find this tiny taste.
This is exactly what I need
to know how to be alive again.
Only a couple months more.
Buds forming on the plum tree,
pushing against its own paper skin
that cover petals about to burst.

A Tuesday Pandemic Love Song

Jenne Hsien Patrick

Tiny little buttercups are taking over the lawn,
loving the poor soil, finding the cracks into the cement
foundation of my house. I even found a leaf threading through

the inside of a windowsill, searching for anything to root
into and grow. When they bloom, their petals blink sunshine
and shimmer and like that, are gone. Like my neighbors

who've abandoned their house in the city. They moved
to an island, to be surrounded by a sea, stretching the hope
of escape against what we are all trying to survive.

I get it.
I'll say it.
None of us wants to die.

My neighbors fear other bodies.
Survival is to pack up and dig in far
from any possible hosts. Here,

near the center of the city with
everyone, even if wombed in houses,
this is what feels safe to me.

I've been eating circus animal cookies
nonstop this entire time, licking the pink
and white frosting off the legs first, popping

the candied confetti against my teeth.
Things with crunch are a sort of echolocation,
they remind me of Oakland and then I might as well

be eight hundred and one miles away at Lake Merritt
with my uncle, the cookies suddenly huge
in my tiny hands. Cookies that all look the shape

of frosted fondant hippopotamus. He and I would sit
here on Saturdays, my mama's oldest brother and little me,
watching the ducks glide in for a watery landing,

waiting for Mama to finish shopping in Chinatown,
buying long beans and jujubes that they didn't sell
at our suburban Food Fair Market and secretly,

I know she loved to be surrounded by her language,
that it felt like home. I could whisper to a cookie,
hold captive a little dream, to be basked in her beaming smile

again, so bright I could feel it as we drove up
in my uncle's plush burgundy Cadillac, my mama waiting for us
at the corner of Ninth and Webster with handfuls of groceries

in plastic bags that all say *Thank you*. Maybe this is the warmth
I am chewing toward here, seeking her sunshine,
crunching each sweet creature in the now, so far away and still

looking for some sweetness, any richness in this soil to root into.

looking for some sweetness,
any richness in this soil to root into

Eleventh Month

Jenne Hsien Patrick

I'm lost in the tall bones
of this empty emerald shell
          city, everything still lit up
all Greek myth-like. Even Chronos,
          he appears and then goes missing.
I bite the insides of my cheeks
          to stop myself from crying.
I found an overwintered daikon, enormous
          and beached, its whole fleshy self
flayed upon the dirt.
          You are only ever nine years old once
and my daughter is never
          going back to her school.
Whatever you thought
          you were going to become
will have to be
          something different now.
Gray-haired auntie, easing
          her wheeled cart up Jackson,
our eyes meet,
          her face mostly covered
by a blue surgical mask,
          a prayer.

March

Hannah Marshall

After "Haute Cuisine" by Amparo Dávila

They hatched in the rain, in the vegetable plots. Hidden
among the leaves, clinging to the stalks,
or amid the damp grasses, they gathered
water beads to make a flute, to garland
the ancient green moss. Nothing much was growing yet,
only wild chives, crocuses, and daffodils. The trees
were just waking as the creatures of dusk clambered
from their puddles like mud-slick dreams.
All the people stayed in their houses, and even the birds
sang in muted taupe. The brick walk undulated. The arches
of culverts and of bare feet, cold. Under abandoned side streets,
antediluvian aphids sang of tunnel, crumble, of robin-fierce anger
and a girl with a sling and two stones. One—a cloud, a spirit.
One—a whirligig, a virus. Rain-gowns draped the architecture,
waterfalling over the gullies. The shining beads were eaten
by mice, and the world had a wedding feast
and there were no airplanes
and there were no dinner dates
and the people all closed their doors
and fewer squirrels chattered at their rubber-burned fellows.
The wakefulness of the vegetable patch went unnoticed
and each thing which woke
found a pink sky and a new bead of water,
and the lace at the edge of things grew
like a webbed mushroom. Everything
was quiet. Everything was fragile.

Community Garden, Wisconsin, Nine Months Pregnant

Hannah Marshall

Originally published in Tiny Seed Literary Journal

Footworn rut, dill weed,
overgrown squash. The vapor
of hose water and hot, early
September. I find trash
buried in the dirt: a '70s era Weeble,
a plastic Dannon lid,
yards of decaying twine.

What rises next spring
depends on me, although the green
is unstoppable, raspberry bushes
ripening berries each year,
abandoned plots overwhelmed
with volunteer tomatoes, their fruits
smaller with each return of warmth.

On Sunday, we sing praise to something
less sure than this adamant garden,
to a hope for light even as nights
elongate across Lake Mendota docks
and Black Earth crops.

Time, what surety can you offer
to our shrinking hold on the earth,
hands like shards of prophecy?
You patiently paint each watered leaf
in gray. You wear away the gravel walk.

In another garden, years from this one,
I will wonder what I thought I was owed that summer.
How my veins pulsed like fiddle strings
in round with the ancient creed
of growing things. Some choices
are made more by wilderness than by us.

Some choices are made
more by wilderness
than by us.

2020 Falls

Hannah Marshall

Cicadas drop from the trees and lie white-belly-up
along sidewalks and ditches.
Sycamore bones twist in the breeze,
the cedar waxwings worship the long spine of the sun.
Each night, the moon disappears a bit more,
clamshell closing on its pearl.
The sunflowers begin to brown, the goldfinches.
Corn dries on the stalk. Hot peppers ripen
in the garden. The air is hazy with pollen.
Coneflowers turn inward
as a turkey vulture hunches heavily on a fence post,
waiting out the final throes.

Crows percuss black feathers against cloud
as we collect sharp bits of glass for the rock tumbler.
Tomorrow, we hope. We say.
We reach the cusp, where growth has burgeoned
and begun to wither,
where apple skins have not yet wrinkled
and the sun has just begun to dissolve
into the edges of a storm.

The geese flee, swirled about in vines of gray light.
Tomorrow a purpled bruise.
Tomorrow the tongue soft against my cheek.
A red bloom of book titles, wanting to be touched.
My desk, wilted marigolds, a pebble.
The curl of my ear, an open shell, the crown of my head,
the blue glass buried there.

Lost Touch

Hannah Marshall

_____

Last night I dreamed people:
riding in a car packed with friends,
walking through a crowded park,
grocery shopping without scrambling back
when someone lurched unexpectedly around a shelf.
Working at the library help desk, the patrons lined up
to the door with books to check out. All night,
I dreamed so many bodies
close enough for me to touch, close enough
to touch me, moist palms,
open mouths. The night was a one-way passage, a trail
of new maple leaves blown from the branches
before a storm.

Lament for March Madness and Remote Learning

Matthew Miller

I stare at wan complexions as I close out
Zoom with my hands up. Most days, school's end
meant evading the hatchets of arms
in the hallway, Tik-Tokkers and backpackers
widening the obstacle. I had to cut and chuck like a
three man weave. Now, the tempo's slowed, a point
guard walking the ball up court to plop in an
armchair. It feels like we've spent three-fourths of
the clock unbuttoning the defenses just to revocate
and call it all off. And I suppose we have that
luxury. We taxi some learning through
YouTube. Students google the lynx, watch
cartoon history tales and stare, with increasing frequency.
They can't seem to crack that clamshell of wonder.
So many just sit, placid as houseplants, buried
in arctic snow. While they are frozen, at least they
won't see the slips I make, trying to get their
attention between the keyway and half-court, trying
to understand context, to see who is open and how I
can get them a shot. They're afraid in a world of
needs. They stutter-step, fumble and pass back.
Some days, I feel my attention is a bouncing ball
that must become the counterweight for their
whole atlas. But I'm tilting on the axis of another chance
lost, so scared of what a turnover might cost.

Infestation

Matthew Miller

I discover the influx of insects,
imperceptible wings infiltrate
whatever cracks we've left
unmasked. Wasps waft lazily.
Red-crowned ladybugs dot
the walls. Flies batter sun-filled
corners. Small indents on window
screens, like how bedsheets cup
her heels. Legs triangled up,
I watch the trajectory of her thumbs
across the keys. She sweeps,
pecks, twists in fits of coughs
and fever. I stand in the door,
swiping stink bugs off the curtain.
As it grows colder, chitinous
contagions spread, making homes
inside ours. She is tapping,
caught between one world and another.
The way of my prayers. Intermittent
flight or cover, eventually crawling toward
some type of light or heat.

The Heat

Cassie McDaniel

I like the heat when I run, the suffocation of air a wet sock in my throat, and the boil of our unforgiving sun on my shoulders. My husband from England says it is self-flagellation; he prefers running at night when headlights prove his existence and mosquitos and bats drop off easily behind him. I tell him it is because I am always shivering, because *he* keeps the air-conditioning too low.

It feels too good to make this jab and I know it isn't true, but I try to compensate anyway: maybe I have low iron. I should buy spinach or take better care of myself, I know that I won't. No one else in the family likes spinach and it wilts in the fridge, a wet mess of green like the scum on our lake. But he is a good man. He lets the scene roll by as if from a car window and I appreciate this about him more than he knows. He is the reason this works, and the truth is we like the way things are. But sometimes I like being somewhere he isn't and the things I find in myself in those dark places.

As I am tying up my shoelaces I bark at the girls to keep the door shut, and they run inside with the speed of small characters in a video game jumping through the rhythmic, chomping maw of a heavy barbed gate slamming closed behind them. My oldest stops to pull the door shut further, squeezing the air from the weatherstripping and turning the deadbolt before catching my eye and then running upstairs.

I don't know if I will ever know what it is exactly, why they prefer to stay in the still and sterile air inside. "Too many bugs," they say.

In video games they battle demons who can disappear and reappear somewhere new, and strange men with double-armed guns and helmets that hide their true faces. They leap off cliff edges and fly through moonscapes and otherworldly structures that sometimes spontaneously explode.

But I sense they are afraid of our towering live oaks with heavy limbs that shake in thunderstorms. Afraid of the spiked feel of grass against the soles of their feet, and the round red-and-black bodies of Jadera bugs that clamber over everything, eating nothing but seeds of trees that shouldn't be there. The uncomfortable thought crosses my mind that I haven't prepared them for the actual world. Another uncomfortable thought: perhaps they are afraid of me, their mother, and my uncompromising pursuit of air-tight seams. I accept their fear as a great mystery to which I may never have answers, because there is nothing else it seems I can do, less turning me inside out and emptying myself right there on the tiled entryway floor. They don't want that. I keep it tight inside and I prepare to go running.

All this makes me feel old and lost, a blip of generational flotsam, my place as an unchanging member of society now complete, unable to understand my own children and their new ways of living.

I step outside, set my watch, and lean into my run as the rolling in of an afternoon storm threatens to overtake my heat and wash me away. I run to keep my family from being too afraid of me. I run to keep my marriage intact. I run to get away from myself, and to save myself too, because everyone can stand me a little bit more after I've run. And I run in the heat to make sure I can feel something.

As the salt of my sweat makes its way through the creases of my face and into the corners of my mouth I close my eyes against the blinding brightness of the sidewalk. I think about veering into the road where cars speed by without concern for a straying pedestrian. My shoes scratch the pavement with each connection my feet make with the ground, and I wonder what it would feel like to misstep, or to fall into a hole where the sidewalk drops off the edge of the Earth. A few seconds later I open my eyes and I am exactly where I expect to be, running by the broken fence and the orange tree with green fruit that belongs to no one.

This air and this heat and these thoughts are old familiar friends. In general I am proud to have survived, to have made it this far. I recall summers of being an outside-child with my nose and cheeks leathered and cracked from sunburn. There might have been aloe, the snap of a stem and the rubbing of green gel onto my sore skin, but I don't remember anyone there but myself. I don't remember anyone fretting, only my secrets: the days following my friend having deposited me back to the driveway of our two-bedroom duplex, peeling away thick layers of dead skin in front of the mirror, as if my own face was once taped to my bones and forgotten about, hardening and tightening, fraying up at the edges over time. I remember enjoying the sting of it being not ready and forcing it anyway. How powerful I felt to unravel my own skin, the raw pink of new flesh sometimes dotting with fresh blood. I would wipe it away until scabs were small and inconceivable on my young face. It isn't something I do anymore but back then we didn't wear sunscreen. We knew about ozone and the hole over Florida but nobody cared. I didn't. I wore my raw-ness like a badge the way that I now run in the heat.

When I return from my run, the girls are playing video games. I shower and then sit on the edge of my bed, looking at a framed picture of our two girls. They are holding hands in front of a university in Lakeland designed by Frank Lloyd Wright, standing atop a midcentury angle where two curbs connect in front of the campus chapel. They are looking at each other. I don't know what they are thinking. Whatever it is seems foreign to me, but it also seems kind and soft, a kindness and a softness I didn't feel for myself until this very moment. For them I hope it lasts. I turn to get dressed and join my husband in the kitchen as he makes dinner.

Later I make the rounds to turn off the various lamps around the house just before my own collapse into bed, and I sneak upstairs to put the thermostat up two degrees, which I know my husband won't notice for a couple of days. After a moment I nudge it up another degree.

The girls are the ages now where they prefer to sleep together, and my tiptoeing across their bedroom floor doesn't wake them. So I do this tonight. They are placid and glowing in the blue halo of their night-light projecting oceanscapes onto the ceiling. I catch a whiff of the baby smell from early motherhood. It is cottoned to their bodies, only detectable now in the still, warm air of night, their white sheets sticking to their skin like bandages. I want this smell to last forever. I want nothing to change. My love is bigger in these moments than I ever allow it to be when we are all awake and yet, tomorrow, I will run again.

I like the things I find in myself in those dark places.

survival
plan

Annie Powell Stone

let's sit on the frame of the clock
knuckles vined around the edge
dangle our feet down onto the face
and drop into time. be swallowed
by that much-revered master, the routine.
that's how we'll get through this
- no -
let's sink into our bodies
breathe and feed. feel and sway.
phototactic
animal no-idea-of-which-day our way along
- or -
let cerebral spaceships carry us
disconnected.
internally preoccupied.
binge-watching into other worlds
here but not here
- wait -
something else?
we'll try anything
(there's time)

stop.
the answer is simple but not easy:
let's sit in the insanity of it all
with masks on,
tune in
and be

sounds like
a hospital

Annie Powell Stone

I.

I haven't checked the weather
since I took the baby for his surgery
maybe because it didn't matter in there
chilled and fluorescently lit,
or maybe because a masked nation
righteously flooded the streets
as I stood by a tiny bedside
giving my scrolling other aims
my search for news from the outside
while holding inside
had nothing to do with the skies
except listening

II.

you might put your finger in your ear
if you wish to block noise
but I have found I can't sleep like this
so instead I use my wrist.
life liquid's pulsing percussion
sending waves to bounce against my ear's drum
the steady signal of my own life
blocking out the hospital noise
partially
a crash cart and a helicopter landing
lend to the night's confusion
and the pounding continues

III.

he sits up
surveying the room from the hospital crib
holding a press conference with the equipment
babbling at shadows.
he is always in the present
little soul, brave boy
and where am I?
in countdown, in fear
I wish I could tell him why and how much
longer it will be
but we don't speak
because we are still inside each other

he is always in the present

Because We Said So

Annie Powell Stone

I thought world-creating
was a job for writers.
Turns out it's also the task
of parents of small children.
They are so little
that their reality is still what we say it is.
Two sides of a heavy coin:
the freedom and the responsibility
of authoring their days.
"Too many people are sick" ---
we can't hide that.
But then anything else is possible beyond.
A walk is an adventure
an old game is a special occasion
realizing the full power of
Because We Said So.
They might not even remember this time,
they're just passengers on a strange ride,
their young minds will forget
--- we hope ---
or maybe they'll always hold it close.

Self-Storage

Kelly Q. Anderson

They have each grown three startling inches. I know because I made the thick, permanent marks on the wooden door that charted their evolving heights. I did it on the morning on their birthdays, when we sang extra loud and blew up balloons to make up for the empty dining room.

Her face is lovely and shaped, no longer filled with the soft, round pillow cheeks of toddlerhood. Pigtails are verboten. "Just a ponytail," she shrugged, over breakfast.

He grew his hair long, became attached to a stuffed Pikachu, and started sleeping in. Three of his baby teeth flew out. He played chess against himself, strategizing black, then white, then black again.

The first mask she ever wore, pink geometric and hand-sewn by my sister, no longer fits. When we drove by her old preschool and I started naming her classmates, she looked at me and said, "I don't remember that." I kept my eyes on the road.

He was able to do masked soccer practice, with mini fields spray-painted in rectangles on the grass. Players could not step into the rectangles of others. They communicated by passing soccer balls. He would often smile with his eyes, but I saw how a quiet moment—a burp from a TV character, the sound of a baseball in a mitt—would remind him that he had no one to share a high five.

The proof is in the Instagram squares and the mock school portraits I took in front of our fireplace (polo shirts paired with sweatpants). So grown. Oh wow. My goodness. *My goodness.*

Later on, I placed the too-small mask in a plastic bin, the clear kind that allows you to see its contents. The tiny square of pink fabric nestled into the rumpled gray pages that bore her wobbly name (always with a backward G). Beside them lay the faded apple cutouts she had taped to the door for the mail carrier, our sole visitor. There's no way the attic can contain all of this, I thought. There's no way.

The Way the World Was

Talya Jankovits

I remember I asked my mother
what it had been like to witness
the world erupt in color. I mourned
trees without a hundred shades
of green, no yellowing edges in autumn,
no orange sun setting sugar maple afire
in a dome of red.

Her laughter made my ears hot.
It only looked that way in old movies
because of the film, not because of the world.
She explained light, photosensitive crystals
and complete blackness to capture
the likeness of color. I felt silly.
I had imagined she lived in shades
of only black and white.

When my own daughter asks me
what it was like when the whole world
put on a mask, I want to laugh at her.
I want to say, *No silly, they only wear masks
because of the way the film was, not because of the world.*
But I nod, I do remember.
I remember

kisses hello on each cheek.
Firm handshakes upon introductions.
The shape of the smile of a passing stranger.
High fives to neighborhood children.
I remember

embraces at large parties where sweat
gathered in beads on foreheads
as bodies crowded dance floors.
The smell of someone's perfume
while standing in line at the movie theater.
I remember

the heat of someone's summer vacation
against my back as we crowded into
photos in front of Fontana di Trevi.
I remember sharing a snack with the man
seated next to me on a redeye, the way his
long legs bumped my knees when he fell asleep.

That's so strange, she tells me
when putting on her mask.
It was wonderful, I tell her.
A pulsing force of living—to know
the shape of a stranger's lips.
I once thought the world was black
and white, I say.
That's crazy—
a world without color!
I nod, adjust her mask.
She tells me:

Sometimes I wish it was like the olden days.
For a brief moment, I think she means
the world in only black and white and I shudder.
Then I realize she wants to see a stranger's smile
and I am filled with hope.

Sometimes I wish it was like the olden days.

Joy

Brett Thompson

Our Saturday morning routine:
a box of Goodie Good donuts in the passenger seat,
baked fresh, hot and glistening
with powdered cinnamon, maple cream, white frosted sugar
as pure as January snow. My daughter in her car seat
belts out Disney songs from my childhood,
her little voice sounding the lyrics across the years
as the sun hits the top of the windshield, radiating warmth
throughout our bodies. This is happiness
I remind myself, because right now, in another country
a woman gazing into her bathroom mirror has buried
all her confidence inside and somewhere else
a doctor amputates a gangrenous arm. Somewhere,
a gymnast has lost her nerve and someone's Baba
has just taken her final breath. So if this is my last act,
sweet sugar on my tongue
and heat and light and the music of my making
I will hold it close and name it for what it is,
joy, resounding affirmations of incomparable joy.

Summer

Brett Thompson

We abandoned the yard.
We slunk down to the basement
and set up our mini Coleman tent
in the cool canned air and laid down
on our backs. Through the nylon,
our flashlights formed shadows
over the ceiling's field. This is about
making due with what is given.
My child's hand still fits in my palm.
The fabric between us and the rest
of the world has frayed. But it is still here
another year. So I take this night.
I press my finger against her mouth.
I blow out the candle.

A Tragedy Unfolding

Brett Thompson

For my sister

My daughters' porcelain baby dolls
Lucy and Lucia, Kinsey doll, Jovie, Donatina
accompany them from room to room,
some ragged, passed down through generations,
others, more recent acquisitions
still with the cardboard packaging
now fashioned into beds. My oldest plays teacher
and reads to them, of plate tectonics, our ever-shifting earth
from her shiny Scholastic magazine.
Should I tell my daughters
that they are the mothers
as immigrants are starving in Queens
and these games of chess continue
to be played by our false gods. Yesterday,
in a southern Connecticut hospital, my nephew was born.
Carter Edward, I wish you all the blessings that you deserve.
I wonder if he can sense all this suffering and despair
or if swaddled close in his mother's embrace
he knows only love, ravaged by light.
He cries for what he cannot know
and when he receives the host, warm and rich,
it sustains him more
than any other
that has yet been named.

Morning
Song

Brett Thompson

In my actual dreams, the world is whole again
and I am out among friends, but more often strangers,
at the park, the cinema, and even once
(in a particular vivid tableau)
a minor league baseball game.
I had no rooting interest except
it was warm and it was summer
with a hot dog golden
in my hands, slathered with relish,
Hunt's Ketchup, and spicy mustard
that was pungent as the stink
of parishioners in an August mass.
Yet, when I awake again, alone
and it is dark and cold,
the furnace yet to click on, the blanket I reach for
still not there, it makes me realize
what has always been hidden,
how I can no longer escape
what any rational person
would term loneliness
just to go out and fill it
with so many other things.

We are dying
like standing water.

Drinking Full Moon Blend During a Pandemic 900 Miles Away from Home

Mel Lake

It was a Brady Bunch night. My laptop screen filled with squares containing grainy faces as more people joined until the grid filled out like the panels of an Alan Moore comic. I didn't know I loved these people until I couldn't see them once a month to talk about comics and life and bullshit in the grimy basement below a coffee shop on Colfax Avenue where none of the chairs matched. To make up for a lack of lights in the basement, they added mirrors. In the coffee shop where we used to meet, the credit card machine frequently went down and the baristas took forever to prepare a latte in a narrow space I never thought was too small until the six-foot rule. When the world stopped, we stopped seeing each other in person and we stopped talking about comics.

"What can't you live without?" Lauren asked.

Every week we talk over screens from our living rooms and shared spaces and balconies. We answer a question, round-robin style. Over the summer, we pondered: "What's your favorite cryptid?" Three of us had laptops propped up outside and our faces changed colors with the bright, atomic-red sunset. Colorado was burning. But on the day we talked about cryptids, apps on our phones told us it was safe to be outside. Ash fell from the sky a few days later, coating the August grass in a strange new snow. A lively discussion ensued about the relative merits of peeing in the woods. Several new cryptids were discovered through research on websites such as The Cryptids of North America and a cryptozoology fan wiki. I had never heard of the one who supposedly haunts the woods around my hometown and looks like an off-brand version of Bigfoot.

What can't I live without?

Coffee.

It was the first thing that sprang to mind. Could I live without coffee? Yes. Would I want to? No. That was my answer. It's true and it reveals absolutely nothing about who I am as a person. I answered first, confident and smiling into the little light on the top of the monitor.

Friends.

Family support.

Travel.

Therapy.

These were the answers my friends proffered to the group as we all nodded into our Hollywood Squares grid. They opened, sharing vulnerable parts of themselves as they talked about missing out on family gatherings and emotional connection. Hugs.

My answer was coffee: a glib answer that, while not untrue, is so unassuming that it completely erases the person behind it.

I didn't say that I like to have coffee from a woman-owned roastery here in Denver because it makes me feel progressive even though the coffee isn't any better than the beans you might get at the grocery store. I didn't mention that I have so many mugs they need an overflow shelf. That I buy mugs that make me happy because they show something about me, even if it's just that I like cats and cute mugs. Sometimes I drink from one stamped with the centennial dates of the library in the town where I grew up. The mug is plain and blue, but it makes me think of the millions of hours I spent in a sweltering attic above the circulation desk, stamping barcodes onto books with a label maker. Finally, Prescott Public Library was going digital, and I helped, one sticker at a time. I got a mug for my efforts.

I didn't tell my friends that I sometimes order coffee from the town I moved away from four years ago, just because having it reminds me of the place I left and secretly wish I hadn't. I pay for shipping from Arizona because the price is the same as the woman-owned beans here and when I see the bags in the mail I remember going to farmers markets in 100-degree heat. The unassuming brown paper bag (compostable,. of course) reminds me of chatting with the amiable roaster dad and his hippy, dreadlocked son about their adventures with the growers in Ecuador. I remember sipping Full Moon Blend at the market on Saturday mornings after a long, hot run on the Rillito River. I ran completely alone, then ambled around the farmers market sipping hot coffee while my shoes stuck to the asphalt. No one understood why I woke up at dawn to run around Tucson before the heat set in, but it was the only time I've ever felt truly remarkable for being me. I can taste the ghost of that feeling in my mug, in the mornings, even though I'm far away from the hot asphalt and the lizards that scurried away from my pounding feet.

I didn't say any of that to my friends.

We've Zoom chatted almost every week since COVID forced us home a year ago. The graphic designer in our group lost her job. Both of the women who worked for the local library systems were furloughed. Relatives contracted coronavirus. Colorado burned. The sky turned orange and the air made us cough. Every week we shared hopes and dreams and thoughts on cryptids.

But I couldn't share anything besides coffee and the fact that I wouldn't be happy without it. Tonight I'm reflecting on why I couldn't—or just didn't—say anything deeper. What I actually couldn't live without. Is it my dog? My partner and family? Writing words? Reading books? Them? The Brady Bunch faces on Zoom squinting at each other and saying things like, "You're on mute," until we all want to scream?

What can't I live without?

What do I live *with*?

I live with chronic pain. Every single day, I load the dishwasher and I want to scream because my hip joints ache with every fork. I live with a depression so severe it puts scars on my arms and, at one point, a tube down my throat. These are the things I would have to reckon with if I actually went through with the thought exercise. What is so essential to my being that I couldn't exist without it? When I wake up and my joints creak and my jaw aches from clenching, I consider. I can live without coffee but I don't want to. How many coffee-filled days drinking out of cute cat mugs while my spine deteriorates can I live *with*?

I didn't tell them because I don't know the answer. I crave the heat of my former life, one where my joints didn't always ache, and I didn't have to peer through a screen at my friends. When this is all over, maybe I'll get the courage to tell them, face to face, what they mean to me. And what my old life meant to me, too. Maybe I'll tell them about the runs on the Rillito and the family who roasted my favorite coffee and how the coyotes chatter to each other if you wake up early enough and run.

But in the meantime, coffee.

What can't I live without?
What do I live with?

I Live on This Island That I've Created

I live on this island that I've created
where the cold winds blow all night
keeping me from sleeping

I live on this island that I've created
where I keep looking out at the horizon
now, my only friend

I live on this island that I've created
where I'm trying to learn, at last,
how to call it home

Walking on Water

Mark Martyre

This morning, as I walked through the wind,
across the La Salle Causeway
I saw a lone fox walking

across the St. Lawrence River
Its delicate scuttle over the ice
was light enough to not break through

to the frigid water below
but heavy enough to land
here in this poem

The fox was alone,
and I wondered if it was lonely
and preferred to be

trotting in the woods,
bustling through town,
or jogging across a grassy field

Something about the reddish coat
cast against the overcast sky,
snow-covered rocks, and bare trees

Maybe there's some metaphor to glean
from that scene
as the fox zig-zagged across the ice,

and through the cold wind,
searching for something,
alone

In Isolation

Mark Martyre

I sit in my apartment
on the bed trying to read,
no music playing this time.

Instead, in the silence,
it's the sounds of the room and building
that are deafening.

There's a hiss and hum
coming from somewhere.
Maybe it's the old pipes, driving me mad.

And I hear the refrigerator rattling
and small motor turning.
A mouse crawling around somewhere.

Finally, it's the sound of my mind
unraveling, coming unglued,
and unspooled.

Like a ball of string
fallen off a shelf, and now rolling across
the cold floor of this apartment,

until it hits a wall at last,
half-undone by circumstance.
I sit, here, alone

---

trying to read.
It's been months
stuck in this never-ending night.

Lying back, into the defeating sound
and silence of the room,
dreaming of the song of the lark

that never arrives.

It's been months stuck in this never-ending night.

Rent/Relief

Glennys Egan

The dog stands whimpering at the closet door. It's two
a.m. and my mind makes monsters of the danger

unseen. Something benign, surely, a mouse or a groaning
pipe. Still, I ask my favorite mage: *Is there reason to be*

afraid? He assures me there are plenty but the apartment isn't
haunted, in spite of its hardwood floors. Disappointment

permeates my relief. I guess the lonely must be getting to me.
I read that in 1912 each floor was fit for an entire family. As if

a girl and her dog can't be just that. How diligently he watches
at our bay window to warn the squirrels away. Safe up here with

two sets of stairs and twelve doors to listen for as the neighbors
come and go. Tail wagging when I reach home. Unbothered by

graffiti in the lobby, fire in the oven, the goddamned faucet
that keeps falling off. And it doesn't matter to him that the man

who built my bookshelves is dead to us now. Maybe
the ghosts will come back when our landlord installs a new sink,

makes good on his promises to patch these walls. Until
then I'll keep learning from the dog how to live not quite alone.

In a Time of
Pandemic

John Jeffire

I.

Garbageman strides Achilles,
Young woman stocking
Grocery shelf floats.
Streets deserted of their
Spiced echoes, wind stripped
Of the scent of faces.
I help the neighbor woman
Corral her dog as she carries
Her shopping inside.
The man across the street
Has added more guns—
Long rifle and sidearm,
When it comes down to it,
The survivalist's full assault
Into your food supply.

My house is empty of all
But myself, my wife, two
Perked dogs awaiting a walk,
The remaining wine and toilet paper.
If I go out hungry, my friends,
                    I go out full

II.

The window, gray landscape.
I am my wife after five brain surgeries,
Limp, trapped in a car pushed
Off the pier, soup spooned
To gasping mouth.
I am a fall of black mane
Writing a candlelight diary
In a frozen attic.
I am five-inch-thick bars and
A green stool on Robben Island,
Mind and hands and manacles
Whetted by limestone.
I am wanderer in a six-by-nine desert,
Four walls the corners of Judea,
Not one temptation to resist.

Bird.
Barren branch teased by wind.
Sudden passing car lightless
Gloved mask at the wheel

III.

The first retreat, inside,
Hearth, water, rice, black tea,
One retreat tailed by another,
Under roof then dig inward,
Mine into dark pith.
Inside, what we stored,
Stacked, froze, buried,
What we locked away
Mostly from ourselves,
Saved for something, someone,
Touching a bare wire, eyes
Burned with acidulant day,
Rummaging the wreckage,
No letter or confession,
Just the dress bought for her
That she never wore, or wore
Smiling for someone else
In some other chamber

IV.

You will flatten curves
for the rest of your days,
and your children, and
                    theirs.
And they won't flatten
because that's the thing
about a curve, how it
refuses to straighten up
no matter how many times
you slap its punk face,
like how not even a hoax
is ever really a hoax if
you must pause before
affirming your own lips,
to feel them as some
stranger's fingers,
stop dead and gather
your purse at every
shadow and footstep,
a man with a screwdriver
to your temple,
every cough a spittle
of death bursting
a Nazi air duct.
And say there are hoaxes—
you can't fully contain them,
and there will never
be a reliable test
or enough of them
even if there were.

These are facts:
boxed bodies line
a trench on Hart Island
and the zippered slump
in recliners in Detroit,
stack themselves like
garment bags in the morgue.
Nothing magically disappears
with spring.
Touch your face.
Breathe your lover in.
It's okay—
all ends cloaked in
distance we never
sought to maintain

Nest

James Croal Jackson

All this nesting leaves me
exhausted. When you awaken
I am too tired to live. One day
the hawk will know this. Sunrise,
the same tender air of earth to feed
new omens. The day a hill
between thunderstorms and ruddy
sunsets, with water neither
ephemeral nor potable.
Quartz trembles and falls
into my mouth. Words
say whatever is in them;
they always fall. A cowbird
on a branch sends out her scent.
(I realize these rocks are symbolic,
a character for which a metaphor
has never been written.) My nest
surrounded by stones has come
to speak in ways that neither
of us can hear. The nest is not
a cage, yet the absence of
a nest is also not a cage.
Inside whichever—I
know you have loved me.

Now That
the End Is
in Sight

James Croal Jackson

Our shared strength wanes—
vaxxed, we talk about the end
like a peek of sunrise through
the blinds. Yes, beyond
winter depression we just had
depression and didn't know
it. Spring sun's out and
we are outside drinking.
Kids graze by like
the virus never happened.
But I was there. I was
strong. Even as a kid,
finding my father crumpled
on the floor and convulsing,
eyes rolled to the back of his
head during his stroke,
I calmly dialed 911
and waited until the
ambulance arrived, and
I was fine the whole time.
But when my sister
screeched her SUV's tires
into our driveway, I let
go. A lifeboat. I ran
into her arms, crying,
not knowing how to say
anything I wanted to say,

and she just held me
and said it's going
to be okay—but she
didn't know. This past
year, I've held you to tell
you it's going to be okay,
but how could I know?
Now that the end is in
sight, we wait for the light,
wilting in its arms to meet it.

I've held you to tell you
it's going to be okay,
        but how could I know?

Orphan

Casey McConahay

Days after they closed the university—after the dorm rooms were vacated, after they locked the libraries and the fitness centers and the rest of the campus buildings—he took the books from his office and put some clothes in his van and then drove north to his parents' house in rural Van Wert County: a house that smelled like dust and neglect and like his father's musty Halston.

No one was there to welcome him. No one made him dinner or soup or coffee. He put some sheets on his bed and put his clothes in the closet. He lit the pilot light on the water heater, and because he'd turned the furnace down to save on the electric bill, the house was cold like a crypt. When he went to his bed and to its cold, twin-sized mattress, he couldn't sleep till it warmed. It took an hour. It was awful.

He'd bought a two-bedroom condo in Upper Arlington because he'd been living with Miranda then, and he'd planned to propose to her. The second bedroom was for the child they'd planned to have together, but now Miranda was gone, and he'd filled the extra bedroom with things he'd moved from his parents' house.

Most of the things that remained in the house were too big for his condo. The sideboard in the dining room barely fit through a doorway. His mother had inherited it from someone. An aunt? Her great-grandmother? He couldn't remember. He wasn't sure what to do about the sideboard—or the table or the stereo system or the hutch in the kitchen.

He took the good set of silver from the drawer in the sideboard. He didn't need it, he knew, but he would take it to his condo. The rest he'd leave for another day. Network newscasts reported that it might be a month—maybe longer—till the lockdowns were lifted.

He'd stay as long as he needed to. He went to Marsh to get some groceries and searched the bare, ransacked shelves. He talked to a clerk at the checkout counter—a teenage boy with an earring.

"Have you been busy?" he asked the store clerk.

"It's not as bad as it was."

"You're out of milk."

"Might be weeks till the truck comes."

He made coffee in the morning and watched the pond from the picture window. Sometimes ducks paddled slowly through the cool springtime water. Sometimes tall, leggy herons fished the pond's weedy shallows.

He sorted books from the bookshelves and drank from mugs his parents had collected on the trips that they'd taken. He used a mug from Seattle—a gaudy Space Needle mug.

He'd keep the mugs. Mugs were good. Mugs were useful.

Because he'd canceled the house's internet service—and because the dean and his students sent him dozens of urgent emails—he ate dinner at Bob Evans and used the restaurant's wireless internet signal. He took a booth in the back so he'd have room for the laptop. The restaurant's tables were much too narrow. He couldn't work at the tables.

His waitress, who wore a surgeon's mask, brought a second Arnold Palmer. He was done with his dinner. He'd placed his fork on his plate edge.

"I won't be long," he told the waitress.

"Stay as late as you want to."

She might have smiled behind her mask. She was thin and blonde and pretty—her eyes and hair: those were pretty. He weighed asking for the waitress's phone number, but she was younger than his students probably. Everyone beautiful was young here. Beautiful women moved to cities—to Columbus. Years ago, when he finished his undergraduate studies, he came back home for the summer. It was during the methamphetamine epidemic, and the women his age had all had children or drug problems.

He didn't want a second Arnold Palmer, but since she'd brought it, he drank it anyway.

Near the pond was an outbuilding where they stored the old metal johnboat. They'd put a small plastic bucket near the door of the outbuilding, and they kept feed in the bucket for the fish in the pond, and when he went to the dock, the fat fish swam toward the dock edge. There were carp and also catfish. He scattered feed in the pond and watched the fish clear the pond of the feed-bits.

They'd caught it late, her doctors told her, but they believed they could treat it. The plan was to be aggressive. They'd do surgery first. Then chemotherapy. If her body responded the way they hoped it would, she would beat it, they assured her.

His mother was encouraged by their optimism, and because her hospital was in Columbus, he'd be close through her treatment. He saw her often in the months that followed, and when she spent the night at the hospital, his father stayed at the condo. It was not a happy time especially—they were worried about the treatments: about how weak his mother was getting—but there were times when he was happy. He was still with Miranda then, and she knew all the city's restaurants, and they would eat with his father, and they'd have nice, pleasant dinners.

When she was able to, Miranda went with him to the hospital. She was there the day they learned that there was nothing more that the doctors could do for his mother, and his mother, weak with illness, held his father and cried, and he cried in the hall with Miranda.

Miranda drove them back from the hospital. He packed a bag at the condo and then rode home with his parents, and he stayed till his mother died in bed three weeks later.

He took the tools from the pegboard in the two-car garage and put the tools in a bucket—tools he'd take to his condo. He had the radio on and opened both of the garage doors, and Mr. Reynolds in the driveway on a green John Deere Gator had a Pabst in his hand and wore a stained set of coveralls.

"I saw your car," Reynolds said.

"Yes, I'm home for a while."

"You out of work?" Reynolds asked. "With this mess with the virus?"

Reynolds took a drink from his Pabst and killed the old Gator's engine.

"I work from home," he said to Reynolds.

"Moving back?"

"No. I'm cleaning."

They walked out back to the pond and to the dock where the fish were. Reynolds scattered the feed and set his Pabst on a dock post.

"They're saying soon—after Easter. No one knows. No one's sure. You think you'll stay till the summer?"

"No. I'll leave when I'm done."

"They'll make us stay in our houses."

"I can stay if I have to."

"Get some masks," Reynolds told him. "Masks and gloves.

Soon we'll need them."

The fish were done with the feed and swam away from the dock, and catfish dove in the pond as Reynolds leaned on a dock rail. Reynolds spat in the pond and took his Pabst from the post.

"I keep them fed," Reynolds said.

"Yes, they hoped that you would."

"They liked these fish."

"Yes, they liked them."

"It's not the same," Reynolds said. "I see this house, and I think of your parents. With them gone—"

"Yes, I know."

"So I feed them."

The following morning, he drank from a mug from South Dakota shaped like the head of Thomas Jefferson. He looked for birds on the pond but saw no birds near the water: only fat little robins in the trees past the window.

He drank the hot, bitter coffee from the president's head and rinsed the mug at the sink before he went to their bedroom. He'd avoided his parents' bedroom—the bed still tousled, unmade, his father's clothes in a heap on the nightstand—and had to force the bedroom's door because it stuck when he tried it. The morning sun through the curtains lit the sheets on the bed and reached a watch on a dresser—a watch his mother sometimes wore—but when he held his mother's watch, its hands were stiff, still, and soundless.

Because there wasn't anyone else to talk to—because his friends were in Columbus, because the clubs were in the city, and they were closed by the virus—he thought of calling her again because he knew that she'd answer.

Sometime after his father's death—when he grew distant without trying to, when there were other things between them that seemed to add to the distance—Miranda left, but she had to. He understood why she had to. She'd been there for all the difficult parts, and though she was living with someone else now, she always answered his calls and let him talk if he wanted. She was good about all of this. She was better about this than he was. He'd call her now, he imagined, and he'd tell her where he was. Maybe she'd come to stay with him, and they could live in this house and feed the fish from the dock, and when they woke in the morning in the bed that they shared, he'd make her coffee and toast, and they'd watch birds from the windows.

When he'd tried all of the dinner specials, he ordered from the breakfast menu. His waitress, whose name was Florence, brought him bacon and pancakes, and he answered his students' emails—ones they'd sent after midnight.

He used the same booth as always near the back of the restaurant. There were many booths to choose from. There were four other diners.

"It's getting worse," Florence told him. "No one comes since the virus."

On the opposite side of the restaurant, diners laughed at their table. They were loud. They were happy. They were done with their dinners.

"It's all that's on the news anymore," a man announced at the table, "but it's not worse than the flu is. It's just a cold. Just a sickness."

He added more of the syrup to his small stack of pancakes as the man at the table crossed his arms on his stomach.

"We're not concerned, are we, Janet?"

"There's not a case in the county."

"They had a case in Celina."

"Only one that I heard of."

He cleaned the grease from the bacon off the keys of his laptop. He took his bill to the counter, and he walked by the table, and a man in a ballcap chewed some ice from his soft drink.

Some of the decisions were easy. Of course he could throw out the hanging baskets in the garage—baskets that didn't have anything in them anymore except the rich-looking potting soil. But what should he do with his dead mother's golf clubs? What about their toothbrushes and bicycles and combs and hats and church shoes?

It was warm and bright and windless, so he went for a run and looked at fields along the road and at a big black-winged vulture.

He hadn't run since Miranda left. She'd been on the cross-country team in college, and it was something they did together. They ran half-marathons in Columbus and Cincinnati and Dayton, but she was faster than he was, and their runs made his knees swell.

He had to rest for a time and caught his breath near the field edge. He started back to the house but only walked—couldn't run—and scared the fat, sated vulture from its prey in the beanfield. Reynolds came in the Gator.

"Need a ride?" Reynolds asked. "I'll drive you back to your home."

"It's my parents'."

It had nothing to do with the death of his mother, and it had nothing to do with the way his father wept when they made the funeral arrangements and through the three-hour viewing or with the way his mourning father spent a month in a bathrobe. It had nothing to do with the calls his father hadn't answered or with the thousand other little things that were said or done or happened between the morning his keening father found her dead in her bed and that day eleven months later when his father, a careful driver, somehow drove in the path of a grain truck.

Home for his father's funeral, he passed the place where it happened. The car had been towed by then, but there were tire marks on the pavement still. Miranda was in the car with him, but when they drove by the spot, he didn't talk to Miranda, and he went alone to the funeral parlor.

Because his father's body was in no condition to display, he had what remained of his father cremated and didn't need to select a casket.

Sometime near the end of his dinner—before she brought the check for his dinner, before he took his check to the counter:

"We're closing," the waitress told him. "By the end of the week."

"Because the state says you have to? Because there's nobody here?"

"Some of both, I suppose. Want a refill?"

She brought a fresh Arnold Palmer when she came from the kitchen, and as he chewed the soft drink's straw, he read the last of his emails. Probably he should have replied to the email, but he didn't want to, so he didn't.

The mug was from Alaska. He'd never been to Alaska. The mug was from a time before their child when they were young and strong and healthy.

A heron fished in the pond, but he did not watch the heron. He took a pair of plastic garbage bags and went to their bedroom. He pulled the clothes from the closet. He set the clothes on the bedspread. He opened drawers in the dressers in the room's dusty corners.

He didn't want to do this—to dig through his father's cotton briefs and the brassieres of his mother. One of the bags was for the clothes he planned to keep. The second was for the clothes he planned to donate. He filled the black plastic bags and worked till late in the day and wasn't done with the clothes, but it was good. It was progress.

Easter had come and gone, and they were still under lockdown. There were protests at the statehouse, but in other states, in other places, they'd put the bodies of the dead in large refrigerator trucks.

He'd sorted clothes in the bedroom. He'd taken the books from the bookshelves. There were boxes in the basement of things his parents had kept, and though some of the boxes held his school pictures and report cards and things he wanted to keep, others he took to the burn barrel at the edge of the property. He burned the newspaper clippings his mother had saved—old issues of the *Times Bulletin* with headlines about moon landings and presidential elections and national championship football games.

He drove to town now and then to pick up things at the supermarket. One night the Bob Evans was dark, and there was a notice on the window.

He no longer checked his email.

He watched the news late at night as he cleaned shelves in the kitchen. There'd been nearly eighty thousand deaths already, and they had no idea how long any of this would last. Politicians talked optimistically about vaccination programs and reopening the economy, but the scientists pled for caution.

He boxed the pans and the pots and the soup bowls.

The boxes he was taking with him were in the back of the moving van. He held a mug from Colorado and took the keys for the van from his pocket.

Reynolds was in the driveway. The Gator's wheels crunched the gravel as it drove toward the moving van.

"Going back?" Reynolds asked him.

"For a while."

"Got it done?"

"I left my bed."

"Nothing else?"

"I left some towels in the bathroom."

Reynolds killed the Gator's engine, and he climbed from the four-wheeler. Reynolds had a Pabst in the Gator, but the beer wasn't opened.

"Heard the latest about the virus?" Reynolds asked.

He gestured toward the moving van.

"The television's in there," he said to Reynolds.

Reynolds leaned to his right to try to look through the van door. The television was on the passenger seat.

"It could last through the fall," Reynolds told him. "We'll lose the Fourth of July and maybe more. Maybe baseball."

Reynolds reached for the Pabst and cracked the tab of the beer can.

"Want a Pabst?"

"No, I can't. I'll be driving."

He spun the keys on a finger. Reynolds drank from the can. The two men looked at the house beyond the big, rented van.

"You think you'll sell it?" Reynolds asked.

"Yes, I think that I will. I think it's time."

"They were good. God, I miss them."

The mug was warm in his hand.

"So do I."

the possum

harps mclean

the dog's asleep
& taking up too much room
        on the bench seat of the old truck
i've been driving all night
from oxford, mississippi

crust of the world crackles
& scratches its back on the night

Lord of ever & every
i am thankful for the abrasive morning sun
snatching shadows of constellations
off the long road

some stick there in the trees
        like autumn
or the mercury bones of birds

new sunlight is arched above the wet grass
suddenly   i realize i am praying

the possum
in the rearview rolls off his back
& goes home to his family

the word shifts from its axis

harps mclean

---

as if on cue
you close your eyes
the vast sky empties of color
& becomes so thin   birds fall out

shadow   the ash of sunlight
darkens & crumbles beneath our feet
like cold burnt paper

the congress of ambulatory birds
crow only consonants

curiously there is no language to share
beyond the compressed layered dreams
no one remembers in the morning

dark knit net of night
swaddles & binds us together
even as the hard black sky
grates the moon into stars
our feet touch &
i know you are here with me

while birds walk into sliding glass doors

Twenty Minutes

Rae Rozman

I was on my way home from the airport.
I'd been visiting you.
It was one of those trips where I could sometimes almost
forget you were sick.
We'd spent the evening drinking expensive gin
and planting purple flowers.

My hair still smelled like the shampoo I left at your house
and my sandals were caked in mud
and everything reminded me of you.

You texted me.
I was in the shuttle, headed to my car.
You told me lightning had struck so close to the shed
the sound shook you to your core,
knocked you over.

I waited twenty minutes for you to tell me you were okay.
Those days, I was always waiting for you to tell me you were okay.

The
Measureless
In-Between

Steve Head

I sent you a multipack
of your favorite crisps
because I don't know
what else I can do.
It felt (still feels) wrong,
carrying on with day-to-day routines,
checking social media feeds,
preparing for a Christmas
that might never come.
I feel like all of this should just stop,
at least for a while,
like the machinery of our lives
should briefly stall
beneath the singular weight
of the moment.

If it weren't for these border closures
and quarantines,
I'd be on the next train underwater
or whatever boat still putters
back and forth across the strait,
to come sit beside you
to talk or listen,
drink countless cups of builder's brew,
and walk along the windblown
clifftop trails, as the low sun arcs
across the gray November waves.

Just be with you,
at the very least,
file off the corners
of your grief-honed days.

But I cannot,
because I am here
and you are there
and the world is a series
of deadbolts
and sterile corridors
and none of us can move.
And we feel each hour
twice as keenly
because there is so little life
to wrap them in.
Far more time
than we'll ever need.

So for now just know
that I think of you,
every morning,
each indistinct evening
and the measureless in-between.

No blood,
but you're my brother.
Hold fast
till our paths reconvene.

I think of you

every morning

each indistinct evening

and the measureless in-between

Last Days
of the
Old World

Steve Head

I'm buying bus tickets
with sofa-back scratch
counting cuckoos in the underground
wondering, in a year or two,
if all this will be gone.
Every night at eight, the
fall of age-old institutions,
laid-off lifers brandish
felt-tip prayers, stood
clinging to their past.

There's a strange new smell
in the streets, like the town's
going bad beneath us.
We notice it from time to time,
walking in circles, carving the
oddest of lives from an hour.
Our world is one square of a map.
A parenthesis.
We walk the same route in reverse,
for novelty.
To see the same things backwards.

There are only bits of shops left.
Barricade tape strung through the
empty aisles like yellow plastic sutures.
I can buy socks, but no shoes.
Gift paper, but no gifts.

There is talk of wearing masks inside
our homes. Booking time slots
at the butcher. Students starving
without handouts. Flowers rotting
on their stems.

Meanwhile, groups of gray-faced men
sit smoking silently outside the
bookies, adamant that this will not
mark the end of things as they were.

It's a nice thought.

But the postman stands at the far end
of the hall, slides my parcel across
the white tile floor, works me into focus
with a latex thumb.
There's a shutter-click and a flash
and I wonder if I'm supposed to smile,
stood there in the same clothes
I wore the day before.
And the day before that.
The stairs smell like bleach,
my breath like smoke.
The postman shrugs and thanks me,
and I tell him it's nothing.
But it's the closest I've been
to a stranger in weeks.

it's the closest I've been
to a stranger in weeks

Distance Between Us

James Roach

I witnessed a kiss goodbye
between two strangers in the rain
before kissing became a crime
and we forgot the feeling of arms
wrapped around our bodies
like gifts,
before we were told to add
more distance
between us.

When spring came,
I vacuumed the cold seasons
out of my car.
Pine needles and small pebbles
clinked their way through the hose
while employees in masks
ran the carwash
for the first time since
we cared
about looking presentable
at the grocery store.
We are only allowed to show
the windows to our tired souls
while we wait in line
to drown in Purell
and watch the chaos
of shelves emptying.

Today, on someone else's grocery list,
I misread grapefruits
as grandparents.
I thought about leaving work
and going to Safeway
dressed to the nines
for oranges
my grandpa could peel perfectly,
the music of Glenn Miller
for him to dance to,
art supplies
my grandma could use
to paint and sculpt a life
without bitterness,
silk flowers
she could plant outside
in the pots by their front door,
and Now 100s brand cigarettes
to further stain her lungs black,
before the Alzheimer's progressed
and she forgot
she used to put cancer to her lips.
I could combine all of the ingredients
and still only summon two ghosts
only to have them
still so distant.

we were told to add more
distance

        between

                us

Number Nine

Alicia Aitken

Forty-seven years you've lived at number nine. Half of the road was still a dirt track leading to open fields when you arrived; now it's bustling with families, dogs, and neighbors with four cars. This was your forever home, four bedrooms and that large sun-trap garden for the children you would have to grow and play in.

Your young arrived quickly, your pride and joy, and one by one they left their childhood home in search of new adventures, starting their own homes and families.

Ten years ago, the house became a home just for you, your partner and companion for so long no longer in this life.

The house has not changed; everything is aging and slightly tattered. The bathroom suite a dull forest green, the floral wallpaper in the bedroom not as vibrant, the pink carpet in the lounge faded from years of service. The net curtains at every window, throwing patterned shadows across your walls when the sun hits, lighting up a trail of floating dust. The grandfather clock filling the silence with its ticking in the hallway, every room holding in the memories, not wanting to forget a single one.

You keep yourself busy, your weekly outing to the shops and coffee the same day every week. You go for a walk at the same time each day, dinner at the same time every evening, kitchen light off once the washing up is neatly done. Lights out at ten thirty every night.

You keep an eye on the street and know all the coming and goings and, more importantly, if something or someone is out of place. You love to talk with people passing by, the postman at the door, the gardener who visits every Wednesday but doesn't really garden much. You store up your words, waiting to share them; at one time you had shared your words with the people who called your home their home too. The words need to escape, loneliness is not your friend, you sit in the once too-cramped house like a loose piece, without a puzzle to complete. Where has all the time gone? It seems only yesterday you were chasing the children, zipping around them, cleaning and tidying on constant repeat, wondering if you would ever know a moment's peace again!

Two weeks ago, I noticed your lights did not turn on, your house still, shrouded in darkness, an invisible coldness creeping over.

Today for the first time in forty-seven years, your house stands empty and silent, only the memories left inside, no one answering the door, no net curtains twitching, no washing up to be done, only traces of the life you led remain.

only traces of the life you led remain

In Orbit at El Camino Hospital

Avalon Felice Lee

An epiphany,   almost: the moon   is only
          an aperture.   You awoke   beneath
a pleiad   of LED   in gravity's   palms.
          Whisper of   atmosphere.   Of callas.   Bed
of pine.   Formaldehyde.   Of nearly.
          Nebulae   crisped into   a jaw-less phantom.
Said   *you will be okay*.   Said   *do you feel*
          okay?   Said   your body   has continued
to continue   in inertia.   In horizontal
          faith.   In a deity   made reliable
by mortality.   (Even the ventilator   knows
          an eon   is too far   to matter.)
Your larynx   mutilated English.   Slit syllables.
          More   beaded phlegm   than sound.
A short-distance   orison.   Or more   a thanks
          to the hands   trained   to reach.

Sheltering

Lisa Romano Licht

I learn
what I cannot contain:
their table's growing clutter,
old mail, empty pill bottles;
the rhythmic hissing
of oxygen
that anchors my father.

A guest in their house,
once my house,
I masquerade.
Quarantined, tested
afraid to share their air,
we eat a room apart,
voices meeting in the hall.

Deep-cleaning rooms
memories rise with the dust:
here we talked after school,
there my friend slept over,
here I felt my boyfriend's hands,
there my daughters, little, dressed my dolls.

At night
I watch TV from the doorway
of my father's room, his coil of air
pet-like at my feet;
we critique million-dollar houses
on the screen.

At night
my mother and I watch
Meet Me in St. Louis,
she on an island of a chair naming
long-dead actors like friends,
me adrift on the couch.

Later, the dining room mirror
mocks my hair roots, tired eyes.
My mother sits across the table.
Naked hair—too long, all gray—
frames her face, creased deeper
by pills counted
no outings, sick friends.

Suddenly, I say, "Put on a mask."
She does.
I cross six feet, turn my face,
hug her from behind.
Noise of surprise,
then arms clutch tight,
we're afloat together.

Ten seconds, maybe more—
my eyes refuse
to meet
the stranded us
of now
distorted in the mirror.

Forced aground again,
I distance from
her wet and grateful eyes.
Ten seconds.
Maybe less.
Our secret.

Outside of Time

Carol Mikoda

As if you could kill time without injuring eternity.
—*Henry David Thoreau*

He thought that was a joke
but here we are killing time, bludgeoning it,
and still it stretches out before us like a carpet
that needs vacuuming, tattered curtains hanging
on either side limiting our vision, cobwebs
stretching down to our faces from god knows what
above us. We have no choice but to keep
walking, step by step, along this corridor
we ourselves constructed, somewhere way back
in intellect's unfolding. We look anxiously ahead.

If only we could sit a spell, let the eternal carpet
roll on without us for a bit. This is hard work,
sometimes paralyzing, and not so productive. Maybe
we can meditate, detach ourselves from this pointless path
and see something more perfectly open, more loving and true,
hidden behind the ripped curtains, where trees
and small animals whisper of our whereabouts
and watch us from a world outside of time.

While You Wait

Carol Mikoda

Gaze on waves until you become the wave, pulsing to shore,
overturning stone and shell, whispering your hiss and roar
into the wind. Listen to the wind until you are the wind itself,
covering miles—over woods, lake, city, highway—admitting
of no obstacle, veering where you will, sheltering birds
on your currents. Watch a bird until you are a bird, so high up
that the earth shrinks, its agonies receding, replaced by focus
on the moment: weather and wind, fish and frog. Your own call
will be all that you hear, backed by water and forest aflutter.
In the woods, curl your hand around that dry leaf until you are
the leaf, poised at the end of a life cycle of spring buds
and green summer glory, about to become the minerals
that will feed the ground from which all will grow.

Delivery

Carol Mikoda

I unwrap the packages of despair
left at the door again
and again; I unfold the envelopes
of sadness crammed in the back
of the mailbox; I click open the emails
of futility that slip past spam filters.
I search for the kernel of joy
hidden in each one
to amplify it and release it
back into the field.

How to Recycle Your Worry

Chandra Steele

Your worry has taken over your space. You boxed it up, but it can't be contained. It seeps out and fills the air around you. It weighs on your skin, it lingers in your lungs.

Your worry has grown so damp and dense that it has spawned a mushrooming suspicion that someone will find you years from now, alone, buried under the weight of all your other worries.

And so you open a window to heave it out or to at least let a little fresh air in. But it's no better out there. The sky is red, the sirens redder. You're going to have to take care of this on your own.

Ninety-nine percent of what you worry about won't happen. Your mother told you this when you were young to stop your persistent panic. But it fed that dread because if you filled your world with worry, maybe you could prevent everything bad from ever happening.

Your mother is gone now, she died right before everyone else fell apart. The ever-present possibility of her death was the root worry that spawned all the other ones. So now you have proof that this law of percentages is a lie, that it behaves oppositionally.

Armed with this new knowledge, you pick up your worries one by one and grind them through a mental algorithm.

You worry that you'll find love on that dating app and will have to delete it, proving its stupid tagline right.

You worry that you'll be serving those canned goods you stockpiled at dinner parties for years to come.

You worry that your wardrobe for warm, warmer, and the warmest weather is going to waste because the climate stopped changing.

You worry that you'll forget to be grateful for all your rights.

You worry that you wasted hours doomscrolling when everything turned out fine.

You worry that you'll live long enough to barely remember this.

it   weighs   on   your   skin

it   lingers   in   your   lungs

Squalor

Shiksha Dheda

The dirt has stuck onto the floor now.
Piles and piles of it.
Covering every inch of my once-immaculate wooden floor.

There are scrunched-up kitchen towels
and small pieces of paper in corners.
The bin is overflowing
with used nitrile gloves and blood-stained tissues.

Used plastics lie on the table,
spilling onto the chair,
onto a mountain of clean laundry
that's been sitting there for months now.

Old Dettol bottles lie strewn in the lower right corner
next to empty glove cardboard boxes.

Six pairs of shoes huddle together in the lower left corner.
Waiting.
Scared for when they'll get doused in disinfecting chemicals.

The leather chair
     worn out now
       being the only place I can sit
        being eroded from repetitive sanitizer burns
has a polystyrene cup full of hot chocolate in its seat.
The drink is probably cold now.

They all look on
         disapprovingly
         dreadfully
         sympathetically
as I enter my twentieth minute of washing my hands,

a few drops of blood now added to the dirt stuck onto the floor.

**been sitting there
for months now**

I'm Seldom Short on Inspiration

Xavier Reyna

is how I used to be.

But I am dry
      these days,
      dry to say
I am four months sober
      twelve months out of seeing friends
            eighteen months past past romances,
      dry to say
      dull as flesh.

And I read through the *New York Times* bestsellers list
and I think about drinking again
just to make their words inspired.

And I sit down to write something better,
      like this,
and I think about drinking again
just to make my words inspired.

But I am dry
      these days,
      dry to say
      dull as flesh
            bubbles matte
              a bad friend
and an even   worse writer.

Eggs

Mo Lynn Stoycoff

It was a terrible time.

One morning I woke up and
made three attempts at preparing
eggs for myself. The first time,
they burned. The second time,
I dropped them on the floor.

The third time, they were overdone
but I put them on the toast anyway.
However, the toast was terrible
(I bought low-carb bread in error!)
so I ended up going hungry.

The whole year was like that.

Glass
Half Full

Steve Denehan

I fell today
under the whole of the sky
and in the grand scheme of things
nobody cared
summer insects continued past
the breeze kept blowing
the day kept moving
toward the evening
toward the night
toward another day

the scream roared up through me
from the bowels of the earth
me, an unwilling conduit
desperately trying to keep it locked behind my teeth
away from my lips
almost succeeding

not a release
as advertised
but a scare for my daughter
a source of shame, a further layer of failure
for me

still balmy at ten to eight
I sit on a deck chair
frustration still bubbling in me
for the time wasted
aware of the irony
of wasting time
by being frustrated
about wasting time

my body, tired and humming with aches
my lips dry
I reach for my glass of blackcurrant
reminding myself to find the joy in little things
it is empty

reminding myself to find the joy in little things

Normal Life

Steve Denehan

The thing is
I don't want it to end
the sunshine
the late nights
the lie-ins
the isolation

I want to keep it all
the secret hideouts
the obstacle courses
the giggling splashes and awful jokes
the trembling ten cent bets of summer evening poker

the sound of moths hitting the veranda lights
the stories that we told
heroes and villains
known only to us
the barbecues
the toasted marshmallows
the silent doorbell
the unknocked door
the only distance being
between us
and the entire universe

it is coming to an end now
or so we are told
the virus, not beaten, but in retreat
I don't want it to end
but they tell us that finally
normal life can resume
whatever that is
or was

Social Distancing

Jan Philippe V. Carpio

May 2020 to January 2021

At some point,
still unknown,
it wore off.

The novelty
they say
goes first,

even the
novelty
of crisis
rises to (or above)
its point
of saturation.

Especially
for those
who live
in houses
brokered
by certainty,

their promises
for all tomorrows
fulfilled today,
and accounted for,

no audits
pending.

Commerce and its
drapery,
hanging
from every corner,
from ceiling to floor,
from floor to ceiling,
its privilege rising,
its stock prayers
falling.

The cleaning lady,

silenced by
the neighboring
chorus
of contamination,
unable to conduct
the symphony
of her chores.

For now,
the dust covers
the casual
violence,
a hit list of
our grocery
transactions,

slowly,
overwhelming,
hands soft (unfamiliar)
unused to

intimate sanitation.

Domesticity
turns tragic,

our laundry list
of (in)competencies
grows longer.

It didn't take
that long
for us.

Have we
stretched to
the ends
of our
indignation?

Have we
reached
the limits
of our
outrage?

Have we
exhausted
the provisions
of our
communion?

Yet,
anxiety's
water marks
remain
visible
at the
perimeter,
its faint
lines, slightly
trembling,
still damp
with worry,
still discolored
with uncertainty.

For the moment,
car horns
no longer
clamor
for release,

it is the people,
quartered
by
quarters.

The pressure
in their chests,
building
to a
bursting,

quietly
unrelenting,

like water
tolerating
the
absurdity
of a dam,

like a
carabao
regarding,
with
indifference,
the child
perched
on its
back
like a
round, flightless
marsh bird.

Instead of arms
rising in the air
hailing taxis,
jeepneys,
buses,
tricycles,

bodies hanging
from tricycles
and train car
ceilings,

bodies packed
like frozen meat,
inside jeepneys,
buses, taxis,

premature fossils,

thawed by
the frictions
of their lost
routines,

old carcasses,

(corpses)
reanimated
by familiar
obligations.

(but what of
the new carcasses
lying bloodless
and betrayed,
and photographed
in conveniently lit
alleyways?)

Instead,
arms now raised
along
unfinished
highways,
palms wide open,
hands now empty,
bodies at a tragic ebb,

voices,

rising
in starving
unison,

muffled by masks,
over the usual masks
we wear,
like foam on the sand,
both left behind,
and washed away
by the tides.

Every day
we trade in
disclosure
and anonymity.

Every day
we bargain with
whereabouts
and disappearance.

Every day
we negotiate with
incarceration
and escape.

Our faces
now,

as rare
as an
eclipse.

the pressure in their chests building to a bursting

Martial Rounds

Jan Philippe V. Carpio

The lone police siren
screams after midnight,
the patrol car makes its
martial rounds,
pulled by a child
holding the string taut,
as it wraps around
the thin, new necks
of these January nights.
no sacristans
with surgical masks
marching through,
their thuribles filled
with gold-en
vac-sins,
frankincense,
and myrrh
(a holy procession
of infection,
the sacrament
of inoculation)
with church bells,
in a steady,
anxious,
rising toll,
echoing
(the strangled
cries of)
the pandemic
Dead.

Parallel Online Funerals

Angel Chacon Orozco

Have you watched a funeral
online already? my friend asks.
Laptop on her knees, turning the screen
toward me. I see a big empty room,
the body of her dead aunt
in the open coffin. I look away,
resenting any pixels in my breath.

Last Friday a volcano awoke
not too far from Reykjavík.
I spent my weekend watching
the livestream of orange glowing,
sassy and all-too-knowing, squeezing
between the carpet like softened
scarabs. This soup of lava
is the only proof I have
that I'm not pickled on pajamas
inside a screen-encrusted jar.

The forecast says it's early spring,
but people keep dying in masses,
our modems wear bandages, and a valley
in Iceland disappears, its sacred
Viking vaults and internet trolls turning
into the ambers of beautiful wounds.
I read of parallel eruptions, mountains
also gone into labor in Sicily and Hawaii
spelling out their epiphanies in blood,
and while I dull myself to sleep,

a fire web underground melts
the hallway of tubes and stretchers
into charcoal toys, panting.

Maybe one day this isolation
will end. Already the magician
swallows the key and never returns.
This is the closest his assistant
will ever get to performing the tricks
on her own, just not yet, not until
she stops staining cigarettes with
the red wine of her lips.

When my grandmother passed
years ago, nobody told me.
I sat in the filthy room
of a foreign country, clueless,
with a broken colossal laptop.
Once she visited me wearing
a moss-covered dress,
I didn't know what to say,
so I listened and listened instead.
It might have been the opposite carrying
its opposite within. The chalk thrown
at the student's forehead as if teaching,
a dormant boy standing indifferent
at the foot of the Popocatépetl,
pocketless corpses being exhumed
if the parents can't pay rent,
or maybe it was something else,
like the fullness we receive
after peaking at the caldera.

When I rose eight hundred
years later, I remembered the day
I watched my first virtual funeral.
How I sat next to my friend, appalled
and at ease, our elbows touching,
the closed eyes of her aunt seen
through wind and the webcam,
her eulogy flashing us in PowerPoint.
When the moment of cremation arrived
everything froze, a crack opened
in the screen and lava heaved itself
into this surface of still things.

This Is a Test

Barbara Simmons

This is a test.
This station is conducting a test of the
Emergency Broadcasting System.
This is only a test.

the old Philco in the corner of the living room
pulled me, a '50s child, into hypnotic visuals,
opened black-and-white Clarabells and Captain Kangaroos
asked me, tested me:
remember my rhymes and measure my manners.

only a test   not the blue book
but a dry run
only a test   that's what the rhythmic sounds
beeped forth, an alarum of sorts

I hear a raven this morning,
from the parking lot where two ravens live,
moving from lamppost to roof,
from edges to corners, their gurgling sounding
deeply from their throats. I'm held by the sounds,
twined with wire, twirled from my car, torqued to listen
to the second-long knocking noises, alerted to a possibility
of danger, waiting for the ending note, a beak's snapping
tapping.

only a test   still
the ravens warn
and wait, is this a test?

Waiting for "And that's the way it is" in the '60s, waiting
for another day that tested who we were, who we
could be, but left alone inside our homes, our cubby holes,
sitting atop our own lampposts, did we wonder if it was all
a test, or was it really happening

CubanMissileCrisisJFKdeadcivilrightsmarchesVietnam
MLKdeadRFKdeadArmstrongAldrinfootstepsonthemoon
smallstepsformanonegiantleapformankindnowshrillfakenews
shrillrealityshrillsoundsunwillingtobeunheard

fastforwardtoimagesweseealongwithwhatweknowasviral
truthacrownwithspikessurroundingvirusonitstwistedgenes
commandingusinvadingusinternallyandchangingourworld
forever.

and how did we learn what we had learned when
we kept hearing the warning sounds, a raven's calls,
the Emergency Broadcast System in all of us
silently signaling
this is not a test
this is my life   our lives
this is your turn to prep
to do a trial run to learn what life's exam will ask of you,

your actions revealing the way
you become the *testum*:
you, an earthen pot, you,
collecting what you need to assay the truth.
No.

This is no longer a test.
This is not even a warning signal.
This is [for] real. Listen.
Listen well. Learn.

07/2020

Zoe Cunniffe

minutes writhing down your back, midsummer gushing. it's july,
       and there's still sickness on the television—
                   the same bodies veiled in plastic,
                   the same undercurrent of bleach,
how you've learned to flinch at the sound of a sharp exhalation.
the numbers still steep, still climbing,
       cloaked in this strange familiarity.
these masses of people on the same pavement, trampling across
children's chalk drawings—painted in march, wiped clean
in july.
       the sun will rise, they said,   but the sky's still black,
everybody lathered in sunscreen, gleaming in photographs:
              mouths wide open,   choking out laughter.
the kids only play outside in packs now—   dead are the
only-child afternoons,   the romance of that lonely thrum,
bicycles pedaled up and down a driveway. the birds sing at two
in the morning, and i listen through the window, every muscle
tensed. there are scratches in the glass now:
              claw marks,   false prayers.
there are words etched in the walls—
       one sentence,   repeated,
              ink growing more and more frayed.
mundane memories,   dulling,   wearing thin.
how i smiled too widely and the roof caved in.   how the sky
turned styrofoam, how your mouth went mechanical.
now we sit on the front stoop, grateful for the touch of hands,
horror crossing strangers' faces when we draw too close.

don't you remember childhood?
        our eighteenth summer dancing like a promise,
    gleaming,   twinkling—   how we would
cut it open at the gut—   a finish line,   a grand opening.
    now july has lost its tender touch.   now the rules shatter
like glass beneath my feet as i scramble, averting my eyes
from everybody with
                skin on skin and
                        mouth to mouth and
        heads cocked back into flashing lights.
the roar of a crowd,   a dying echo,   a reverberation,
            and here you are,   living in an artifact.
how do i reconcile with this empty space,
                            this suffocation,
when you breathe the same tainted air you always did?

how do i reconcile with
this   empty   space

skin on skin

Zoe Cunniffe

last night:
blinking consciousness,
                          a surfacing.
here in this room of immaculate oxygen,
                          this silent echo chamber—
    another world rising from the floorboards.
the hallway cramped,   a shoulder-knocking sensation:
    someone by your feet,
                          someone by your side.
        the stroke of skin on
                              skin,   the way hands brush,
                  a simple kind of swelter.
you bled love,   finger-painted it across the walls.
    how your knees used to buckle,
              and now you tuck them to your chest.
how the sun sweeps across the sky,   and even the light
    does not touch you.

tonight, though—
you are sixteen again,
standing in the school bathroom.
              the echo of voices,   the slam of stall doors,
                      mascara brushes flicked across lashes.
tonight,
you bend forward against the mirror,
          and yours is not the only face reflected in the glass.
it wraps around you on teeth-chattering nights—
          your tears on strangers' shoulders,   feet clattering,
                  those slight smiles on the stairway.
      so withered, so   dreamlike.

this it what you trace the memories for—
        that careful collision,   the transfer of breath.
you cling to it
from the blue light glow of your bedroom,
        the latency of voices
                rising and dying
                        like phantoms.

a surfacing

washington monuments

Zoe Cunniffe

---

in the old world, it wasn't so   tender:
     the click as i buckle my seatbelt,
   the flicker of headlights,   the ring of the radio.
another voice,
    rippling like water,   sounding clear above the static.
now i grip the door handle   and peer out the window
  like a child,   rain speckled on the glass,
     stoplights smearing in the storm.
can't we pretend   we've just been to a concert,
the residue of a crowded room   dusting our cheekbones?
we used to beat our hands together as the lights dimmed,
     selling ourselves the rhythm of a room.   strangers,
      scattered,   the fizz of soda in a styrofoam cup,
the pound of music still thrumming in our ears   as we spilled
    out onto the sidewalk.   it was that hush of knowing
what you had shared:
   a lingering headrush,   a flooding,
     gleaming phosphorescent   through your body.
can't we pretend   we're taking the long way home,
    meandering around the monuments,
waving at lincoln out the window?   he still sits so solemn,
      staring at the lights across the bridge,
   the skyline reflected blue-gold on the water.
don't look at the   shuttered doors, the stark sidewalks,
  a city gasping for air.   look at the dashboard,
all lit-up,   and breathe it in— this peaceful desolation,
  a calm like we'll never know again.

Contributors

Alicia Aitken lives in Essex, United Kingdom, and loves to write short stories. Alicia is a busy mother, paddleboarder, avid reader, and traveler. You can follow Alicia on Twitter at @aliciaaitken01.

Kelly Q. Anderson is a writer and journalist for lifestyle publications. She served as a newspaper columnist for six years until the pandemic torpedoed local news. Presently, she is a student at Cornell University's eCornell (Diversity and Inclusion Program), as well as StoryStudio in Chicago. She is an active member of Off-Campus Writers' Workshop and holds two degrees from the University of Iowa.

Jan Philippe "JP" V. Carpio is a writer and filmmaker living in the Philippines. His writing has been published in national publications like *Philippine Graphic* and the *Philippine Star*. His films have been screened and cited at various local and international film festivals. He teaches at the digital film-making program of the College of St. Benilde School of Design and Arts and the film program of MINT College.

Jan Chronister is a retired writing teacher with more time on her hands than she ever expected. She has published four chapbooks and two full-length poetry collections and currently serves as president of the Wisconsin Fellowship of Poets. You can find her online at janchronisterpoetry.wordpress.com.

Kelle Schillaci Clarke is a Seattle-based writer with deep LA roots. Her work has recently appeared or is forthcoming in *Superstition Review*, *Pidgeonholes*, *Barren Magazine*, *Lunate*, *Cotton Xenomorph*, and *Bending Genres*. She is on Twitter at @kelle224.

Zoe Cunniffe is a poet and singer-songwriter from Washington, DC. She has previously been published in literary journals such as *Blue Marble Review*, *New Reader Magazine*, *Doghouse Press*, and *Velvet Fields*. Zoe can be found on Instagram at @there.are.stillbeautifulthings.

Steve Denehan lives in Kildare, Ireland, with his wife Eimear and daughter Robin. He is the author of two chapbooks and two poetry collections. Twice winner of *Irish Times*' New Irish Writing, his numerous publication credits include *Poetry Ireland Review*, *Acumen*, *Prairie Fire*, *Westerly*, and *Into the Void*. He has been nominated for Best of the Net, Best New Poet, and the Pushcart Prize.

Shiksha Dheda uses poetry (mostly) to express her OCD and depression roller-coaster ventures. Mostly, however, she writes in the hopes that someday, someone will see her as she is: an incomplete poem. Sometimes, she dabbles in photography, painting, and baking lopsided layered cakes. Her work has been featured or is forthcoming in *Off Menu Press*, *The Daily Drunk*, *Kalahari Review*, *Brave Voices Magazine*, *Anti-Heroin Chic*, *Versification*, and elsewhere. You can find her on Twitter at @ShikshaWrites.

Glennys Egan was raised in the Canadian prairies and now lives in Ottawa, where she works for the government like everyone else. Her poetry appeared in *Capsule Stories Winter 2020 Edition*. She has also been published or is forthcoming in *Taco Bell Quarterly*, *Funicular Magazine*, *The Aurora Journal*, and several other lovely places. You can find her and her dog, Boris, online at @gleegz.

Paulette K. Fire is a writer in Boulder, Colorado. Her work has appeared in *Harvard Review, Carve Magazine, The Pinch, The Jewish Literary Journal, Lilith,* and *Alaska Quarterly Review* (forthcoming). Her essay "Presumably Murdered" was chosen as a notable essay by *The Best American Essays 2019.*

Bethool Zehra Haider is a law student from California. She enjoys writing about the moon, shades of purple, and peonies. Find her at @bethoolzehra.

Steve Head is a poet and novelist from the leafy dullness of the London suburbs. He started writing poetry as an attempt to decrypt the unfathomable weirdness of adolescence and continued when he realized that it made him appear somewhat cooler than he actually is. Steve's debut poetry collection *Blueprints* is available now via Amazon.

Teya Hollier (she/her) is a mixed raced Black woman living in Toronto, Ontario. She is a recent graduate of York University's creative writing program, in which she won both the Babs Burggraf Award and the Judith Eve Gewurtz award during her studies. Her writing aims to confront racial oppression, mental illness, and generational trauma. She loves horror movies and is currently working on a collection of short horror stories that are allegorical explorations of the Black experience.

Ashley Huynh is a senior at UCLA studying psychobiology and minoring in professional writing. When she is not doing clinical research, teaching undergraduate life science, or working as a medical assistant, she loves to write personal essays and creative fiction. Check out her work on Instagram at @huyblogs.

James Croal Jackson (he/him) is a Filipino American poet working in film production. He has one chapbook and two forthcoming: *Our Past Leaves* (Kelsay Books, 2021), *Count Seeds with Me* (Ethel, 2022), and *The Frayed Edge of Memory* (Writing Knights, 2017). He edits *The Mantle Poetry* from Pittsburgh, Pennsylvania. You can find him online at jamescroal jackson.com.

Talya Jankovits has published work in a number of literary journals. Her micro piece "Bus Stop in Morning" was a winner of a *Beyond Words Magazine* writing challenge. Her short story "Undone" in *Lunch Ticket* was nominated for the Pushcart Prize. Her poem "A Woman of Valor" was featured in the 2019/2020 Eshet Hayil exhibit at Hebrew Union College Los Angeles. She holds her MFA in creative writing from Antioch University and resides in Chicago with her husband and four daughters.

John Jeffire was born in Detroit. In 2005, his novel *Motown Burning* was named Grand Prize Winner in the Mount Arrowsmith Novel Competition, and in 2007 it won a Gold Medal for Regional Fiction in the Independent Publishing Awards. His first book of poetry, *Stone + Fist + Brick + Bone*, was nominated for a Michigan Notable Book Award in 2009. His most recent book, *Shoveling Snow in a Snowstorm*, a poetry chapbook, was published by Finishing Line Press in 2016. For more on the author and his work, visit writeondetroit.com.

Mel Lake lives in Denver with a partner, chronic pain, and a very good dog. She has an English BA and an MS in technical communication. She is a technical writer in the corporate world by day and a creative writer the rest of the time. Her first publication is forthcoming in *The Human Touch*.

Sukriti Lakhtakia is currently pursuing her master's in literature at Shiv Nadar University, India. Lately, she has been preoccupied with birds and, in particular, with the Indian gray hornbill, which eludes her. She writes at riutski.wordpress.com.

Avalon Felice Lee is an Asian American Californian. Her work is published or forthcoming in *Kissing Dynamite*, *JUST POETRY*, *Right Hand Pointing*, *Bluefire*, *Plum Recruit Mag*, and elsewhere. She has been recognized by Scholastic Art and Writing Awards, Leyla Beban Young Writers Foundation, *National Poetry Quarterly*, *The Lumiere Review*, and *Ringling*, among others. You can find her and her kitten, Esky, on Instagram at @avalonfelicelee.

Lisa Romano Licht is a lifelong New Yorker who writes poetry and creative nonfiction. Her work has appeared in *Ovunque Siamo*, *Mom Egg Review*, and *The Westchester Review*. Her prose poem "Dead Birds Everywhere" is forthcoming in the *Train River* COVID-19 anthology. She holds an MA in writing from Manhattanville College.

Hannah Marshall lives in south-central Illinois, where she works as the advising editor for Greenville University's literary journal, *The Scriblerus*, and as the poetry editor for Converse College's literary journal, *South 85 Journal*. Marshall's poem "This Is a Love Poem to Trees" will appear in *The Best American Poetry 2021*. Her poems have also been published in *Poetry Daily*, *New Ohio Review*, *The South Carolina Review*,

North Dakota Quarterly, and elsewhere. She received her MFA in creative writing from Converse College.

Mark Martyre is a Canadian writer and musician. He released six full-length studio albums between 2012 and 2019. He's received nominations for Toronto's Best Songwriter and has also written songs for a play that went on to be performed in Toronto and at the SpringWorks Festival in Stratford. Also a published poet, Mark has been published in literary journals and online magazines such as *Capsule Stories, Spadina Literary Review, The Mystic Blue Review, Twist in Time, Verdancies, Postcard Shorts*, and *Aberration Labyrinth*. In 2019, Mark self-published a collection of poetry.

Casey McConahay has work published in *december, Lake Effect*, and *Southern Humanities Review*. He lives in northwest Ohio.

Cassie McDaniel has published poems and fiction in *Human Parts, Used Furniture Review, Split Quarterly*, and *The Mangrove Review*. She lives north of Orlando. Say hi on Twitter at @cassiemc.

harps mclean is a husband, father, poet, and painter. His relationship with language is complicated. They mostly tolerate each other with foregoing jealousy, distrust, and a one-sided codependency. His poems have appeared in *Stickman Review, The Cape Rock*, and *Sugar House Review*.

Linda McMullen is a wife, mother, diplomat, and homesick Wisconsinite. Her short stories and the occasional poem have appeared in over ninety literary magazines. She received Pushcart Prize and Best of the Net nominations in 2020. She may be found on Twitter at @LindaCMcMullen.

Carol Mikoda used to teach writing and new teachers. Some of her work has appeared in *Grief Becomes You, Acta Victoriana,* and *Children, Churches and Daddies.* She lives in upstate New York where she walks in the woods, photographs clouds or treetops, sings, and plays guitar as often as possible.

Matthew Miller teaches social studies, swings tennis rackets, and writes poetry—all hoping to create home. He and his wife live beside a dilapidated orchard in Indiana, where he tries to shape dead trees into playhouses for his four boys. His poetry has been featured in *Whale Road Review, River Mouth Review, Club Plum Journal,* and *Ekstasis Magazine.*

Beth Morrow is an author, teacher, and memoirist who lives in Ohio. Her work has appeared in *Creative Nonfiction,* the *Brevity* blog, *JMWW, Small Leaf Press,* and the *Columbus Dispatch.* Connect with her on Twitter at @Buckeye_BethM, on Instagram at @Buckeye_BethM, or her blog, BethMorrow. blog, where she writes about the intersection of writing and life.

Angel Chacon Orozco is a video creator and editor with a background in journalism that lives in a queer community in the Netherlands. He discovered the joys of poetry studying at the International Writers' Collective in Amsterdam, and in his daily life he enjoys all shapes of writing, film, and fermentation of crooked courgettes.

Jenne Hsien Patrick (she/they) is a writer and an artist currently based in Seattle. She incorporates text into textiles, papercutting, and stop action animation and creates spaces for healing and storytelling in her community. Jenne has work published or forthcoming from the *Asian American Literary Review* and *wildness*. You can find her online at jennehsien patrick.com.

Deborah Purdy lives outside Philadelphia where she writes poetry and creates fiber art. She is the author of *Mermaids in the Basement* (dancing girl press, 2021). Her work has appeared in *Cleaver Magazine, American Poetry Journal, Heron Tree, Mom Egg Review*, and other publications.

Xavier Reyna is a poet from the Rio Grande Valley.

James Roach (he/him) is a trans poet in Olympia, Washington, who does his best work between the hours of up-too-late and is-it-even-worth-trying-to-sleep? His latest work can be found in Google Drive gathering dust while he makes edits and wonders if this time warp will ever end.

Rae Rozman (she/her) is a poet and educator in Texas. Her poetry, which often explores themes of queer love (romantic and platonic), loss, and education, has been published in several literary magazines and anthologies. An avid reader, you can often find her curled up in a sunny corner with a mug of coffee, a big white bunny, and a novel. You can find her on Instagram sharing poems, book reviews, and pictures of her two adorable rescue bunnies at @mistress_of_mnemosyne.

Barbara Simmons grew up in Boston and now resides in San Jose, California. The two coasts inform her poetry. A graduate of Wellesley College, she received an MA in The Writing Seminars from Johns Hopkins. Retired, she savors smaller parts of life and language, exploring words as ways to remember, envision, celebrate, mourn, and try to understand more. Her poem "This Is a Test" arises from the many ways our quarantining has pushed us to listen more closely, and incessantly, to warnings about our world's and our health. Publications have included *Santa Clara Review*, *Hartskill Review*, *Boston Accent*, *New Verse News*, *Soul-Lit*, *300 Days of Sun*, *Capsule Stories*, and *Perspectives* on KQED, the NPR local affiliate.

Chandra Steele is a writer and journalist from New York. Her work has appeared in *No Contact*, *Wigleaf*, *Storm Cellar*, *Ample Remains*, *Vol. 1 Brooklyn*, *McSweeney's Internet Tendency*, *Entropy*, and others. Rick Moody once said she wrote the best description of a racetrack he has ever read. She has never been to a racetrack. More of her writing can be found online at chandrasteele.com.

Annie Powell Stone (she/her) has a BA in English from the University of Maryland and an MS in urban education from the University of Pennsylvania. Her poetry has appeared or is forthcoming in *Door Is a Jar*, *Rising Phoenix Review*, and *Second Chance Lit*, among others. She loves peanut butter toast and summer mornings. She lives in Baltimore, Maryland, with her husband and two kiddos. Read more of her poetry on Instagram at @anniepowellstone.

Mo Lynn Stoycoff is an autodidactic poet whose work has appeared or is forthcoming in *Poetry Now*, *Rise Up Review*, *South Broadway Ghost Society*, *California Quarterly*, *Speckled Trout Review*, and other journals and anthologies. Mo works in the performing arts and lives on the colonized land of the Patwin people in Central California.

Melissa Sussens (she/her) is a queer South African veterinarian and poet. Her work has appeared in *Germ Magazine*, *Ja. Magazine*, *Odd Magazine*, and *The Sock Drawer*, among others. She is a small animal vet by day and by night a poet and editor involved in Megan Falley's Poems That Don't Suck online writing courses. She lives in Cape Town with her girlfriend and their two dogs. Find her on Instagram at @melissasussens.

Brett Thompson has been writing poetry since his graduate days at the University of New Hampshire, where he earned an MA in English writing with a concentration in poetry. He has been published in various journals, including *Plainsongs*, *Tilde*, *District Lit*, *The Literary Nest*, and *Cobalt Review*. He teaches and lives in New Hampshire with his wife and two young daughters.

D. H. Valdez teaches social studies and humanities at his former high school. He holds a master's degree in teaching from the University of Washington. He and his wife Holly grew up together in Seattle and continue to live in the city with their son. Valdez has previously been published in *Lunch Ticket*, *The Citron Review*, *Flash Fiction Magazine*, and *Lost Balloon*. He desperately awaits the return of the Seattle SuperSonics.

Editorial Staff

Natasha Lioe, Founder and Publisher
Natasha Lioe graduated with a BA in narrative studies from University of Southern California. She's always had an affinity for words and stories and emotions. Her work has appeared in *Adsum Literary Magazine*, and she won the Edward B. Moses Creative Writing Competition in 2016. Her greatest strength is finding and focusing the pathos in an otherwise cold world, and she hopes to help humans tell their unique, compelling stories.

Carolina VonKampen, Publisher and Editor in Chief
Carolina VonKampen graduated with a BA in English and history from Concordia University, Nebraska and completed the University of Chicago's editing certificate program. She is available for hire as a freelance copyeditor and book designer. For more information on her freelance work, visit carolina vonkampen.com. Her writing has appeared in *So to Speak*'s blog, *FIVE:2:ONE*'s #thesideshow, *Moonchild Magazine*, and *Déraciné Magazine*. Her short story "Logan Paul Is Dead" was nominated by *Dream Pop Journal* for the 2018 Best of the Net. She tweets about editing at @carolinamarie_v and talks about books she's reading on Instagram at @carolinamariereads.

April Bayer, Reader
April Bayer is an MA student in English literature at the University of South Dakota. She graduated with high distinction from Concordia University, Nebraska in 2019 with a BA in English and theology and a BS Ed in educational studies. When she isn't busy teaching her students about literature and composition, she enjoys writing poetry, playing with cats, and researching the works of Willa Cather. Her work has previously appeared in *Potpourri* and *Capsule Stories Isolation Edition*. April joined *Capsule Stories* as a reader in November 2020.

Stephanie Coley, Reader

Stephanie Coley is a country girl from Gering, Nebraska. She graduated in 2016 from Concordia University, Nebraska with a BA in English and a minor in art. She has been a journalism teacher, janitor, data technician, and more. Stephanie is a published poet, appearing in the National Creativity Series of 2009 and *Mango* Issue 3, Respeto, in 2017. She is also a winner of the 2020 Historic Posters Reimagined Project, which can be found at the Nebraska History Museum in Lincoln, Nebraska. Stephanie currently works as the program manager at the West Nebraska Arts Center in Scottsbluff, Nebraska. Stephanie joined *Capsule Stories* as a reader in January 2021.

Rhea Dhanbhoora, Reader

Rhea Dhanbhoora worked for close to a decade as an editor and writer before quitting her job and moving to New York to get her master's degree and finally writing the stories everyone told her no one would ever read. Her work has appeared or is forthcoming in publications such as *Sparkle & Blink*, *Awakened Voices*, *Five on the Fifth*, *Capsule Stories Autumn 2020 Edition*, *Fly on the Wall Press*, *HerStry*, *Artsy*, *Broccoli Mag*, and *JMWW*. Her work has been nominated for a Pushcart Prize and Best American Essays. She is currently on the board of directors for the literary organization Quiet Lightning and editor of RealBrownTalk. Rhea joined *Capsule Stories* as a reader in January 2021. She's working on several projects, including a linked story collection about women based in the underrepresented Parsi Zoroastrian diaspora. You can read her work online at rheadhanbhoora.com.

Hannah Fortna, Reader

Hannah Fortna graduated in 2016 from Concordia University, Nebraska, combining her passion for the written word and her affinity for art making with a degree in English and a minor in photography. After a three-year career as a freelance copyeditor, she heard traveling calling her name and now works seasonal jobs in places connected to America's national parks. When she's not selling souvenirs to tourists in gift shops, she enjoys hiking, photographing natural spaces, and writing about the flora and fauna she saw while on the trail. She reads anything from poetry to middle-grade novels, but the nature-inspired creative nonfiction section is her haunt in any bookstore. Her poetry has previously appeared in *Moonchild Magazine* and *Capsule Stories Spring 2019 Edition*. Hannah joined *Capsule Stories* as a reader in November 2020.

Kendra Nuttall, Reader

Kendra Nuttall is a copywriter by day and poet by night. She has a BA in English with an emphasis in creative writing from Utah Valley University. Her work has previously appeared in *Spectrum*, *Capsule Stories*, *Chiron Review*, and *What Rough Beast*, as well as various other journals and anthologies. She is the author of the poetry collection *A Statistical Study of Randomness* (Finishing Line Press, 2021). Kendra lives in Utah with her husband and poodle. When she's not writing, you can find her hiking, watching reality TV, or attempting to pet every animal she sees. You can find out more about her work at kendranuttall.com. Kendra joined *Capsule Stories* as a reader in January 2021.

Rachel Skelton, Reader

Rachel Skelton graduated from William Woods University with a BA in English, a concentration in writing, and a secondary major in business administration, a concentration in management. She has interned for Dzanc Books and now works as a freelance fiction editor specializing in speculative fiction. You can find more information about her work at theeditingskeleton.com. She occasionally tweets about editing at @EditingSkeleton and talks about books she's reading at @TheReadingSkeleton on Instagram. When she's not doing anything reading-related, she's hanging out with her cats, collecting houseplants, and attempting to learn how to crochet. Rachel joined *Capsule Stories* as a reader in January 2021.

Deanne Sleet, Reader

Deanne Sleet is a graduate of Saint Louis University with a BA in English, a concentration in creative writing, and minors in African American studies and women's and gender studies. She has interned for *River Styx* and Midwest Artist Project Services, where she gained experience with grant writing, editing, and writing copy. She is currently the leasing and marketing manager at City Lofts on Laclede and holds the secretary position for SLU's Black Alumni Association. She writes short fiction and poetry, and a novel is in the making. In her spare time, she hangs out with her cat and roller-skates. Deanne joined *Capsule Stories* as a reader in February 2021.

Claire Taylor, Reader

Claire Taylor is a writer in Baltimore, Maryland, where she lives with her husband, son, and a bossy old cat. Her writing has appeared in a variety of publications and has received nominations for the Pushcart Prize and *Best American Short*

Stories. Claire's first publication at age ten in *Highlights Magazine* was a poem about what it might feel like to be a leaf. Nowadays, her work focuses largely on themes of motherhood and mental illness. In addition to writing for adults, Claire is the creator of Little Thoughts, a monthly newsletter of stories and poetry for children, and she has written several picture books that are searching for publishing homes. A selection of Claire's work is available online at clairemtaylor.com. Claire joined *Capsule Stories* as a reader in March 2021.

Submission Guidelines

Capsule Stories **is a print literary magazine** published once every season. Our first issue was published on March 1, 2019, and we accept submissions year-round.

Become published in a literary magazine run by like-minded people. We have a penchant for pretty words, an affinity to the melancholy, and an undeniably time-ful aura. We believe that stories exist in a specific moment, and that that moment is what makes those stories unique.

What we're really looking for are stories that can touch the heart. Stories that come from the heart. Stories about love, identity, the self, the world, the human condition. Stories that show what living in this world as the human you are is like.

We accept short stories, poems, and remarkably written essays. For short stories and essays, we're interested in pieces under 3000 words. You may include up to five poems in a single poetry submission, and please send only one story or essay at a time. Please send previously unpublished work only, and only submit to one category at a time. Simultaneous submissions are okay, but please let us know if your submission is accepted elsewhere. Please include a brief third-person bio with your submission, and attach your submission in a Word document (no PDFs, please!).

Find our full submission guidelines and current theme descriptions at capsulestories.com/submissions.

Connect with us!
capsulestories.com
@CapsuleStories on Twitter and Facebook
@CapsuleStoriesMag on Instagram

CPSIA information can be obtained
at www.ICGtesting.com
Printed in the USA
LVHW010934230721
693407LV00006B/125